# The PHYSICS

## *of*

# FLIGHT

*by*

## ALFRED LANDÉ
*Professor of Physics, Ohio State University*

REINHOLD PUBLISHING CORPORATION
330 West Forty-second St., New York, U.S.A.

1945

Copyright 1945 by
REINHOLD PUBLISHING CORPORATION

PHYSICS DEPT.

This book has been manufactured in conformity with U.S.
Government regulations governing paper and book production.

*Printed in the United States of America by*
THE HADDON CRAFTSMEN, INC., SCRANTON, PA.

# Preface

When looking for a textbook on aerodynamics of the airplane for students after their first year of college physics and algebra, the author found a certain gap between elementary introductions and more advanced representations which require a full knowledge of calculus. The present book tries to fill this gap by including Reynolds' law of similarity, the vortex theory of induced drag, and the mechanics of the gyroscope. A reader looking for integral signs will find only a few of them with proper explanations on the spot. Differential calculus has been used outside the text only in some footnotes for the convenience of more advanced readers. On the other hand we have omitted the characteristic curves of special wing types and other subjects of less general interest in favor of a discussion of unconventional aircraft, in particular the autogyro, the helicopter, the jet plane, and the robot bomb.

Alfred Landé

Columbus, Ohio
August, 1944

# Contents

# Chapter I

# General Principles

### 1. Introduction

It has often been said that flying was made possible by the invention of the internal combustion engine, with its great power and small weight. This statement is quite justified as long as one thinks only of the task of forward *propulsion*, modern rocket- and jet-propelled craft notwithstanding. Of equal importance, however, is the problem of *sustentation* and its successful solution by the streamlined wing or airfoil. The airfoil, with its long span and curved ("cambered") cross-section, its blunt leading edge and sharp trailing edge, is an almost perfect instrument of pure sustentation. An inventor without previous knowledge might expect that the best instrument of motion through the atmosphere would be a pointed dart cutting its path through the air with the least possible resistance. In order to obtain a greater measure of stability he might improve his dart into an arrow or flatten it into a board whose long axis, however, would still point into the forward direction of travel. It is a most surprising fact that much better results are obtained from a *transversal* vehicle which opposes the air with its whole broadside, *i.e.*, the wing. The physical explanation and evaluation of the amazing qualities of the transversal wing as a means of sustentation consitute the chief topic of this book.

The wing and its relative, the propeller, have attained their present degree of efficiency only after a long series of theoretical investigations and experimental tests in aerodynamic laboratories and in actual flight. Most of this research work was concerned with the problem of increasing the upward force of *lift* and reducing the resistance, or *drag*, of the wing. Whereas a flat board travelling through the atmosphere offers a lift-to-drag ratio of 6 to 1, the same ratio for a wing has been raised to the amazing value of 20 to 1, so that an engine thrust of one pound sustains a load of twenty pounds.

The aerodynamic principles which were developed originally for the wing of the airplane may also be utilized for the construction of efficient *propellers*. Aside from the work of propulsion, however, the airscrew raises a new dynamic problem because of the gyroscopic deviation from the intended change of direction during turns and other maneuvers. A discussion of this effect is needed also for an understanding of various gyroscopic instruments of *navigation* which have contributed so much to the technique of blind flying and automatic piloting.

The story of aviation may be said to have begun with the mythical flight of Icarus whose wings were built by his father Daedalus and held together with wax. When he flew too close to the sun the wax melted, and he fell into the sea. An early scientific attempt to investigate the conditions of flight was made by Leonardo da Vinci about 1500. He weighed various birds and found that their weight in Florentine pounds was the square of their wing spans in yards; his conclusion was that a man weighing 144 pounds would need wings with a span of 12 yards.

The first practical steps in the direction of the modern airplane were taken by Cayley in England, who carried out extensive experiments with large glider models (1810). All attempts to drive an aircraft with steam power failed. Success came only through a combination of the newly invented gasoline motor with the gliding wing. Pioneer work in this direction was done by Sir Hiram Maxim in England, S. P. Langley in the United States, and Otto Lilienthal in Germany. The latter lost his life during a glide of his craft from the top of a precipice. The first actual flight from the ground under engine power was achieved by Orville and Wilbur Wright. On Dec. 17, 1903, at Kitty Hawk, North Carolina, they flew a distance of 852 feet in 59 seconds with a pusher-type biplane of their own design. Other pioneers of aviation were Santos-Dumont and Blériot in France, Hargrave and Burgess in the United States, and Cody and Dunne in England. The superiority of the monoplane over the biplane was established in 1909 by Blériot's 37-minute crossing of the English Channel.

The present trend of aviation is directed toward airplanes capable of climbing to extreme altitudes and travelling at tremendous speeds over long distances. Great progress has also been made in the opposite direction, that is, constructing wingless aircraft which derive their lift from a huge horizontal airscrew or rotor. It may well be that *autogiros* and *helicopters* rising vertically from the ground, hovering motionless over an object, and travelling leisurely over short distances at low altitudes, will dominate the lower strata of the atmosphere while airplanes are designed for higher and higher altitudes.

Airplane dimensions have undergone vast changes since the Wright brothers built their 16-hp four-cylinder biplane with a wing span of 40 feet carrying a gross weight of 750 lbs. For dimensions of modern airplanes refer to Table 2.

Military airplanes are divided into various *types*, *i.e.*, bombers, pursuit planes, transports, etc. Modifications of a type are designated as *models*. A list of military types is given in Table 1. Table 2 gives the speed, weight, size, and engine power of various models.

Table 1.   Types of Military Planes

| Army | | Navy | |
|---|---|---|---|
| A | Attack | VB | Bomber |
| AT | Advanced trainer | VF | Fighter |
| B | Bomber | VG | Single-engine transport |
| BC | Basic combat | VN | Trainer |
| BT | Basic trainer | VO | Observation |
| C | Cargo | VP | Patrol |
| F | Fighter | VR | Multiple-engine transport |
| P | Pursuit | VS | Scouting |
| PT | Primary trainer | VT | Torpedo |
| PB | Two-place pursuit | | |
| LR | Long range | | |

## 2.   Relative Wind; Wind Tunnels

When a solid body moves through air, the mutual force between any part of its surface and the adjacent air has two components. One component is perpendicular to the surface ("normal component"), and its magnitude per unit of area is known as *pressure*. The other component is parallel to the surface ("tangential component") and is similar in nature to the *friction* between two solid surfaces. The pressure at any point of the surface may be measured by a small barometer concealed inside the body and communicating through a tube with the surface point in question.

The mutual force between any part of the surface and the adjacent air depends only on the *relative* motion of the body with respect to the air. That is, the wind force at any surface point does not change when the body and the surrounding atmosphere are transferred as a whole in any direction with constant velocity. In particular, the wind force on any part of the surface is the same in the following three cases:

(a) when the solid body travels with constant velocity $V$ to the left through still air;

(b) when the solid body is fixed in space and exposed to a steady wind
   to the right, of velocity $V$;
(c) when the body travels to the left with velocity, $v$, into a wind of
   velocity $(V-v)$ to the right.

The fact that the wind force depends on the relative motion only
is important for the practical measurement of the pressure distribution

Table 2.   Specifications of Various Models.

| Model | Speed (mph) | Weight (tons) | Span | Length | Hp |
|---|---|---|---|---|---|
| A-25 Curtiss Helldiver | 300 | $7\frac{1}{2}$ | 49'8" | | 1700 |
| A-29 Lockheed Hudson | 300 | | 65'6" | | 2×1350 |
| B-17 Boeing Fortress | 300 | 24 | 103'9" | 74' | 4×1200 |
| Bd-2 Douglass Havoc | 320 | $6\frac{1}{4}$ | 61'4" | 47'3" | 2×1600 |
| B-24 Consolidated Liberator | 300 | 23 | 110' | 63' | 4×1200 |
| B-25 N. Amer. Mitchell | 300 | 12 | 67'6" | 54' | 2×1350 |
| B-26 Martin Marauder | 325 | 12 | 65' | 58'2" | 2×2000 |
| B-29 Boeing Superfortress | 300 | 55 | 141' | 98' | 4×2200 |
| P-38 Lockheed Lightning | 400 | $6\frac{3}{4}$ | 52' | 38' | 2×1150 |
| P-39 Bell Airacobra | 350 | 4 | 34' | 29'9" | 1150 |
| P-40 Curtiss Warhawk | 380 | $3\frac{1}{2}$ | 37'4" | 31'8" | 1260 |
| P-47 Republic Thunderbolt | 400 | $6\frac{3}{4}$ | 40' | 35' | 2000 |
| P-51 N. Amer. Mustang | 400 | 3 | 37' | 32'2" | 1520 |
| PV-1 Lockheed Ventura | 275 | | 65'6" | 51'2" | 2×2000 |
| Pan-American Clipper | 190 | 41 | 152' | 106' | 4×1650 |
| 98 De Havilland Mosquito | 400 | $9\frac{1}{4}$ | 54'2" | 41'2" | 2×1350 |

NACA Wind tunnel

over an airplane. Instead of investigating the wind force in actual flight, a small model plane may be suspended in a *wind tunnel* and exposed to an artificial wind of variable speed under various barometric pressures so as to duplicate actual conditions of flight at various speeds from sea level to extreme altitudes at various temperatures. A recently constructed wind tunnel contains two $35\frac{1}{2}$-foot propellers producing an air stream of 120 miles per hour over a cross-section of $30 \times 60$ feet. Only the innermost part, 8 feet in diameter, is used for actual tests, to insure uniform wind distribution over the model. A new giant Boeing wind tunnel in which air combat conditions at extreme altitudes are duplicated has been constructed in Seattle. An 18,000-hp electric motor drives the air through a concrete tunnel at the rate of 700 miles per hour, five times as fast as a natural hurricane. A special refrigerating plant cools the air to any desired temperature down to $-67°$ F which is the constant temperature of the stratosphere beginning at 36,000 feet.

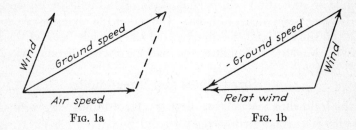

Fig. 1a          Fig. 1b

In actual flight one has to distinguish between *ground speed*, that is, the speed over the terrain, and *air speed*, or speed relative to the atmosphere. As air speed is produced by the propeller thrust, ground speed is the vector sum of wind and air speed:

$$\text{ground speed} = \text{wind} + \text{air speed (vector relation)},$$

as illustrated by Fig. 1a. The air speed is of opposite direction and of the same magnitude as the *relative wind:*

$$\text{air speed} = -\text{relative wind},$$

so that the former equation may also be written:

$$\text{relative wind} = \text{wind} - \text{ground speed (vector relation)}$$

(see Fig. 1b). The wing splits the airflow in two parts which join again farther downstream, so that the relative wind has different values at different points near the disturbing wing. The relative wind occurring in the last equations refers only to the *constant* undisturbed airflow far from the airplane.

**Problems**

(1) An airplane takes off at an air speed of 50 miles/hr. If a 20-mile wind blows *parallel* to the runway, at what ground speed does the plane leave the runway? The same, if the wind blows at a 30° *angle* across the runway?

(2) An airplane travelling at 120 miles/hr runs into a down current of 20 miles/hr. Find the angle between the horizontal course and the relative wind, and the strength of the relative wind at the instant of entering the current.

(3) An airplane glides at an angle of 10° with a horizontal speed component of 40 miles/hr. After it encounters a head wind, the gliding angle changes to 25°. How strong is the wind?

(4) A bomber is seen travelling north at 60 miles/hr ground speed through a 30-mile/hr west wind. A pursuit plane of 180 miles/hr air speed spots the bomber exactly east of itself. Construct the direction of the pursuit plane on the map and the directions of the propeller axes of the two airplanes. Find the time of interception if the original distance was 25 miles.

### 3.   Streamlines and Streamtubes

In the following sections we first try to obtain a *kinematic* description of the disturbed airflow past a solid body. Then we turn to the *dynamic* explanation of the forces responsible for the disturbed air-

Fig. 2a                    Fig. 2b

flow, and to the forces of reaction on the solid body itself. Let us consider the airflow past a solid body from the wind-tunnel standpoint, case *b*, p. 10, with a body at rest in a steady wind. The air is compelled to deviate from its original straight course not only along the surface itself but also at a considerable distance before and after passing the body. The advantage of describing the airflow from the wind-tunnel standpoint lies in the fact that the air particles are streaming along certain fixed lines past a fixed body. (An exception occurs in the case of turbulence; see p. 24). A picture of the steady *streamlines* past a cylinder with axis perpendicular to the wind is shown in Fig. 2a, and Fig. 2b depicts the flow past a thin plate. In both cases the bodies are supposed to have infinite "span" perpendicular to the flow in order to yield *two-dimensional flow*, represented by the two dimensions of the plane of the paper and every other parallel plane. Compare with plate C on page 22.

Fig. 3 depicts the flow past an airfoil, supposing again that the span (perpendicular to the plane of the paper) is infinite. The original "irrotational" flow (Fig. 3a) is soon transformed into stream-line flow (Fig. 3b). For details refer to section 21.

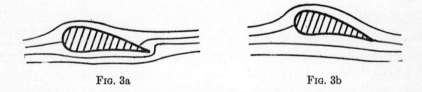

FIG. 3a                    FIG. 3b

Figs. 2 and 3 show only a small number of streamlines; they are selected so as to be *equi-distant* far in front of the obstructing body. The intervals between adjacent streamlines contract or expand, however, near the body. The space between two streamlines is called a *streamtube*. A three-dimensional streamtube is obtained by considering a small cross-section area far from the body, and taking the streamlines emerging from the edge of the cross-section as walls of the tube. The amount of fluid passing per unit of time through a certain cross-section is the same at all times, according to the definition of steady flow. Furthermore, the mass of fluid passing per unit of time through one cross-section of a certain streamtube is equal to the mass passing per unit of time through any other cross-section of the same streamtube. If it were not so one would obtain an accumulation or depletion of fluid between two cross-sections of the tube, which is in contradiction to steady flow. The constant rate of flow within a streamtube may therefore be measured across *any* cross-section of the streamtube. The rate of flow equals the product of the cross-sectional area, $a$, the velocity, $v$, and the mass per unit of volume or density, $\rho$. Although $a$, $v$, and $\rho$ may vary along the streamtube, the product $av\rho$ represents the mass flowing per unit of time through any cross-section of the tube, and is constant along the entire length of the individual streamtube in steady flow past a body at rest:

$$av\rho = \text{constant along a streamtube}$$

If the fluid is incompressible, so as to have constant density, the product of the two other factors, $a$ and $v$, alone remains constant:

$$av = \text{constant}$$

along a streamtube in an *incompressible* fluid. The last equation tells us that *the velocity, $v$, is inversely proportional to the cross-sectional area of the streamtube if $\rho$ is constant.* Although air is a compressible fluid, the density of the air along a streamline remains practically constant, so that the rule, $av$ = constant applies to air, except in the case of large pressure variations along the length of the streamtube.

The last equation may also be written in the form $av = AV$, that is: the product of cross-section and velocity at any point along a streamtube, $av$, has the same value as the product $AV$ on the same streamtube far from the obstructing body. As an example, consider Fig. 3b. The streamtubes contract above the wing and widen below it. Therefore, *the air speed is increased above and reduced below the wing* as compared with the wind velocity, $V$, far from the wing. This velocity distribution is the chief source of the force of *lift*.

Modern pursuit planes have speeds comparable to the velocity of sound (1088 ft/sec = 740 miles/hr). The pressure variations along the wing under these conditions are so large that the density can no longer be considered as constant, which means that the complete formula, $av\rho$ = constant, must be taken into account.

The streamlines of Figs. 2a, 2b, and 3 run past the solid body without coming in contact with the surface. There is one streamline, however, which terminates vertically on the body. The point of perpendicular incidence is known as the *stagnation point*. The relative wind velocity, $v$, at the stagnation point is *zero*, since both the perpendicular and the tangential component of the flow vanish (under wind-tunnel conditions). The stagnation point in two-dimensional flow diagrams actually represents a *stagnation line* parallel to the infinite span.

## 4. Bernoulli's Theorem

As a first approximation, air may be considered as a frictionless fluid of *constant* density, which implies a *constant* value of the product

$a \times v$ along a streamline, although $a$ and $v$ themselves may vary from point to point. The lack of friction means that the transformation of kinetic into potential energy takes place without loss.

Let us discuss the *dynamic* reasons for the variation of the velocity $v$ along a streamline. The kinetic energy per unit of volume may be called the "kinetic energy density." Its value is $\frac{1}{2}\rho v^2$. The kinetic energy densities at two points, $A_1$ and $A_2$ along the same streamline are $\frac{1}{2}\rho v_1^2$ and $\frac{1}{2}\rho v_2^2$, respectively. The increase of the kinetic energy density from $A_1$ to $A_2$ thus is

$$(\tfrac{1}{2}\rho v_2^2 - \tfrac{1}{2}\rho v_1^2)$$

There are two reasons for this increase. *First*, if point $A_1$ is located at altitude $h_1$ and $A_2$ at altitude $h_2$, the air "falling" from $h_1$ to $h_2$ suffers a decrease of its potential energy of a magnitude equal to $(\rho g h_1 - \rho g h_2)$, where $g = 32.2$ ft/sec.$^2$ *Secondly*, if the air at $A_1$ and $A_2$ has pressures $p_1$ and $p_2$, respectively, the air is forced from $A_1$ to $A_2$ by the pressure drop $p_1 - p_2$. The work of this pressure drop on every unit volume of air* is

$$\text{work} = (p_1 - p_2)$$

This work together with the decrease of the potential energy $\rho g h$, contributes to the increase of the kinetic energy. We thus arrive at the energy equation per unit volume of air:

$$\tfrac{1}{2}\rho v_2^2 - \tfrac{1}{2}\rho v_1^2 = (\rho g h_1 - \rho g h_2) + (p_1 - p_2).$$

Both sides of the equation are measured in ft-pdls/ft$^3$ = pdls/ft$^2$, when $\rho$ is measured in lbs/ft$^3$ and $v$ in ft/sec.

Rearranging the last equation we arrive at the relation:

$$\tfrac{1}{2}\rho v_1^2 + \rho g h_1 + p_1 = \tfrac{1}{2}\rho v_2^2 + \rho g h_2 + p_2.$$

That is, the sum of kinetic and potential energy density, plus pressure is the same at point $A_1$ as at point $A_2$, when $A_1$ and $A_2$ are *any* two points on the same streamline. Therefore

$$\tfrac{1}{2}\rho v^2 + \rho g h + p = constant \ along \ a \ streamline$$

in the steady flow of a frictionless fluid of constant density. This is

---

* A volume element of the streamtube of area $a$ and of length $dl$ may be under the pressures $p$ and $p - dp$ at its two cross-sections. When the volume element $adl$ is shifted in the direction of lowering pressure through the distance $dl$, the work done is "force times distance," namely, $ap - a(p - dp) = adp$ multiplied by the distance $dl$. The work on the volume $adl$ thus is $(adl)dp$. The work per unit of volume is $dp$, when the unit of volume is shifted through the pressure difference $dp$, and the work on a unit of volume shifted through a finite pressure difference is $p_1 - p_2$.

*Bernoulli's theorem.* At constant or practically constant altitude ($h_1 = h_2$) the law simplifies to

$\frac{1}{2}\rho v^2 + p = $ constant along a streamline (Simplified Bernoulli theorem).

Altitude differences along an airplane are so small that variations of the potential energy, $\rho gh$, of the air along a streamline may be disregarded altogether, in agreement with the simplified form of Bernoulli's theorem given above: the pressure along a streamline decreases at the same rate as the kinetic energy density, $\frac{1}{2}\rho v^2$, increases.

Fig. 3b shows the streamlines past a wing. They are crowded together along the upper surface. This signifies, according to section 3, that the air speed is increased above the wing; hence the air pressure (dynamic pressure, $p$) above the wing is reduced as compared with the

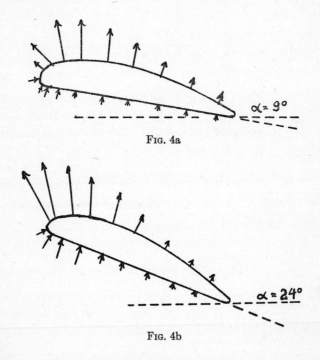

Fig. 4a

Fig. 4b

normal pressure far from the wing (static pressure, $P$). The opposite is true below the wing. The upper wing surface thus suffers an upward *suction*, whereas the lower surface receives *excess pressure*. Both together produce an upward force of *lift*. Figs. 4a and 4b give graphic pictures of the pressure and suction per unit of area, indicated by arrows toward and away from the surface, for the same wing under two different angles of attack. The figures show that, contrary to popular ideas, the greater part of the lift is due to suction above the wing, and only a minor part is due to excess pressure below.

## 5. Applications of Bernoulli's Theorem

Bernoulli's simplified theorem may be written in the form

$$\tfrac{1}{2}\rho V^2 + P = \tfrac{1}{2}\rho v^2 + p;$$

$V$ and $P$ refer to points far from the body, whereas $v$ and $p$ are the air speed and the dynamic pressure at any point near the body. It is not necessary to specify the streamline on which the latter point is located, since $P$ and $V$ are the same on all streamlines far from the body. The units in the above formula are

$\rho$ in lbs/ft³,  $\qquad$  $v$ in ft/sec,  $\qquad$  $p$ in pdls/ft²

or

$\rho$ in slugs/ft³,  $\qquad$  $v$ in ft/sec,  $\qquad$  $p$ in lbs/ft²

A slug equals 32.2 pounds.

*Example:* A stream of slightly compressed air of density $\rho = 0.08$ lb/ft³ and of velocity $V = 50$ ft/sec is forced past a solid body. It is observed that near a certain surface part two adjacent streamlines approach half their original distance. How large is the suction per square foot?

*Solution:* Bernoulli's equation yields for the excess pressure

$$p - P = \tfrac{1}{2}\rho(V^2 - v^2) = \tfrac{1}{2}\frac{0.08}{32.2}(50^2 - 100^2)$$

$$= -9.33 \text{ lbs/ft}^2$$

The example shows that, in spite of doubling the speed from 50 to 100 ft/sec, the suction is only a small fraction of the ordinary atmospheric pressure of $14.7 \times 144 = 2116.8$ lbs/ft².

The kinetic energy density, $\tfrac{1}{2}\rho v^2$, depends on the density of the air, $\rho$; at standard temperature, 15° C or 59° F, and at normal atmospheric pressure the standard value is

$$\rho_0 = 0.07651 \text{ lb/ft}^3 = 0.002378 \text{ slug/ft}^3.$$

Table 3 gives the density of air at various altitudes in terms of $\rho_0$. The temperature changes from an average of 15° C at sea level to − 55° C ( − 67° F) at 40,000 feet, and remains almost constant at higher altitudes. The stratosphere begins at about 36,000 feet. The last column of the table will be used in section 41.

Table 3.   Density of Air at Various Altitudes.

| Altitude (ft) | Pressure (lbs/inch²) | Temperature (°C) | Density ratio $\rho/\rho_0$ | $\sqrt{\rho_0/\rho}$ |
|---|---|---|---|---|
| 0 | 14.7 | 15 | 1.000 | 1.000 |
| 1,000 | 14.1 | 13 | 0.971 | 1.051 |
| 5,000 | 12.2 | 5.1 | .861 | 1.077 |
| 10,000 | 10.05 | − 4.8 | .737 | 1.165 |
| 15,000 | 8.31 | − 14.7 | .629 | 1.261 |
| 20,000 | 6.82 | − 24.6 | .532 | 1.371 |
| 25,000 | 5.42 | − 34.5 | .449 | 1.492 |
| 30,000 | 4.37 | − 44.4 | .373 | 1.637 |
| 35,000 | 3.48 | − 54.3 | .307 | 1.804 |
| 40,000 | 2.72 | − 55.0 | .246 | 2.016 |

*Standard pressure* may be expressed in various units as follows:

$$p_0 = 14.7 \text{ lbs/inch}^2 = 2117 \text{ lbs/ft}^2$$
$$= 76 \text{ cm of mercury} = 29.92 \text{ inches of mercury}$$
$$= 10.33 \text{ meters of water} = 1.033 \text{ kg/cm}^2$$

The density ratio in the fourth column of Table 3 is calculated from the second and third columns as follows: according to the general gas law, the value of $pv/T$ for a certain gas is always the same, when $p$ is the pressure, $T$ is the absolute temperature, and $v$ is the volume per unit of mass.   Instead of $v$ one may write $1/\rho$, where $\rho$ is the mass per unit of volume, so that the gas law reads $p/\rho T = \text{const.} = p_0/\rho_0 T_0$; hence $\rho/\rho_0 = (p/p_0)/(T/T_0)$.   Here $p_0 = 14.7$ and $T_0 = 273 + 15 = 287$ are the standard conditions.   At 25,000 feet one finds $p = 5.42$ and $T = 273 − 34.5 = 238.5$; hence $\rho/\rho_0 = (p/p_0)/(T/T_0) = (5.42/14.7)/(238.5 /287) = 0.449$, in agreement with the table.

*Example 1:*   A water pipe has a diameter of 3 inches except for a constriction 1 inch in diameter.   When a pressure of 1/50 atm. in excess of normal pressure is applied to the wider part of the pipe, the water is observed to move 9 inches/sec in the wider part.   How large is the excess pressure in the narrow part?

*Solution:*   The density of water is $\rho = 62.5$ lbs/ft³ $= 1.94$ slugs/ft³; the velocity, $v_2$, is derived from $v_2 a_2 = v_1 a_1$, where $v_1 = \frac{3}{4}$ ft/sec, $a_1 = \pi/64$ ft², and $a_2 = \pi/400$ ft²; hence $v_2 = 4.66$ ft/sec.   With 1 atm. $= 2117$ lbs/ft², Bernoulli's equation yields

$$\tfrac{1}{2} 1.94(\tfrac{3}{4})^2 + 2117/50 = \tfrac{1}{2} 1.94(4.66)^2 + p_2$$

The excess pressure, $p_2$, is obtained in lbs/ft².   The additional standard pressure, $p_0$, cancels on both sides of the equation.

*Example 2:* An airplane flying at an altitude of 10,000 ft and at 150 miles/hr develops relative wind of 300 just above, and 80 miles/hr just below the wing. If the wing area is 160 ft², how large is the force perpendicular to the wing?

*Solution:* The density at 10,000 ft, according to Table 3, is $\rho = \rho_0 \times 0.737$ = 0.001756 slug/ft³. Above and below the wing we have equality of $p_1 + \frac{1}{2}\rho v_1^2$ and $p_2 + \frac{1}{2}\rho v_2^2$ with $p_0 + \frac{1}{2}\rho V^2$ far away. Hence $p_2 - p_1 = \frac{1}{2}\rho(v_1^2 - v_2^2)$, that is,

$$p_2 - p_1 = \frac{1}{2}0.001756[(300 \times 44/30)^2 - (80 \times 44/30)^2]$$

in lbs/ft². The factor 44/30 transforms miles/hr to ft/sec. The resulting force, $F$, is $(p_2 - p_1) \times 160$ lbs perpendicular to the wing.

Bernoulli's theorem applied to a *stagnation point* ($v = 0$) reduces to the important equation

$$\tfrac{1}{2}\rho v^2 = p - p_0 \text{ at the stagnation point.}$$

That is, the excess pressure $p - p_0$ at the stagnation point equals the kinetic energy density of the relative wind, $V$. The wind speed in the tunnel, or the air speed of an airplane in flight, may thus be found from a measurement of the *gauge pressure* at the front stagnation point. (A rear stagnation point does not exist because of eddy formation. This is a frictional effect, whereas Bernoulli's theorem applies to a frictionless fluid).

*Example:* The pressure at the front stagnation point of a wing is found to be 2 cm of mercury in excess of the barometric pressure. What is the speed of the airplane at 5000 ft?

*Solution:* The density at this altitude, according to Table 3, is $\rho$ = 0.002378 × 0.861 = 0.00205 slug/ft³. A pressure difference of 2 cm corresponds to 2117 × (2/76) = 55.6 lb/ft². Thus $V$ is obtained from the equation $\frac{1}{2} \times 0.00205 \times V^2 = 55.6$; hence $V = 235$ ft/sec = 160 miles/hr.

Pressure differences are measured most conveniently by Pitot tubes or Venturi tubes. The *Pitot* static tube has one "dynamic" mouth facing the wind and one "static" mouth protected from the wind. The difference between the dynamic and the static pressure may be measured by a barometer whose two surfaces communicate with the two ends of the Pitot tube. The *Venturi* tube consists of a wind-receiving cone of comparatively large solid angle, and a discharge cone of smaller solid angle, connected coaxially through a constriction. If the cross-section area of the latter is $a$, and the mouth area of the receiving cone is $A$, the air velocity through the throat will be $A/a$ times the wind velocity, $V$, entering the mouth, that is, $v = VA/a$, if the density is not changed materially. The pressure difference between mouth, $P$, and throat, $p$, may be measured by a barometer. Bernoulli's theorem yields the relation

$$P + \tfrac{1}{2}\rho V^2 = p + \tfrac{1}{2}\rho V^2 (A/a)^2$$

so that, *vice versa*, the wind velocity is obtained from the inverted formula of Pitot

$$V^2 = (2/\rho)(P-p)[(A/a)^2 - 1]^{-1}.$$

$(P - p)$ is measured in lbs/ft$^2$ and $\rho$ in slugs/ft$^3$.

## 6. Adhesion and Viscosity

The aerodynamic process which leads to the production of lift and drag cannot be understood without studying the *adhesion* of the air to the surface of the wing, and the *viscosity* or internal friction (stickiness) of the air itself. It should be remembered that Bernoulli's theorem is valid only as long as friction is neglected.

*Adhesion* is the force which compels the air, wherever it is in direct contact with a solid body, to stay at rest relative to the surface rather than to glide over the surface. Adhesion disagrees with the streamline patterns of Figs. 2 and 3, which show streamline flow moving over the surface with finite velocity. These patterns are valid only outside of a thin layer surrounding the surface of the solid body. Within this *boundary layer* the relative wind increases gradually from $v = 0$ on the surface itself, as required by adhesion, to the $v$-value represented by the streamline patterns of Figs. 2 and 3. Because of the narrowness of the boundary layer, the streamline patterns may still be used for deriving the pressure distribution over the surface of the solid body, according to Bernoulli's theorem. The perpendicular pressure, however, is accompanied by a tangential force known as *skin friction drag*. The latter has its origin in the shearing forces of the air within the boundary layer.

Shearing forces of viscosity appear whenever parallel layers of a fluid glide over each other. A quantitative measurement of the *viscosity* of a fluid is obtained in the following way. Take two horizontal metal plates of area $S$ and of small perpendicular distance $d$. Fill the gap between them with the fluid in question, fix the lower plate, and move the upper plate parallel to it with velocity $V$. Due to adhesion, the fluid in contact with the upper plate will also move with velocity $V$, whereas the fluid near the lower plate will stay at rest. The force necessary to keep the upper plate moving against the shearing forces of the fluid in the gap is directly proportional to the velocity $V$, and to the plate area $S$, and inversely proportional to the distance $d$ of the plates; briefly,

$$F = \mu V S/d$$

where $\mu$ is a factor of proportionality called the *coefficient of viscosity* of the fluid; $\mu$ is large for molasses, and small for air; it varies with temperature but is almost independent of pressure. It is convenient to characterize the internal friction of a fluid by the ratio of $\mu$ to the density $\rho$, and to call this ratio *kinematic viscosity*:

$$\mu/\rho = \nu = \text{kinematic viscosity}$$

Values of $\nu$ at standard pressure and temperature are given in Table 4.

Table 4.   Values for Kinematic Viscosity.

| $\nu$ | ft²/sec | cm²/sec |
|---|---|---|
| air | 0.000158 | 0.148 |
| water | 0.000014 | 0.013 |

If the air pressure and therefore the density are doubled, then $\nu = \mu/\rho$ decreases to half its original value, since $\mu$ is practically independent of the pressure. As the dimension of $\nu$ is "area/time," or "length $\times$ velocity," the product of length times velocity divided by kinematic viscosity, $lV/\nu$, is *dimensionless*.

When a certain solid body at rest is exposed first to a stream of water and then to a stream of air, both of the same velocity, $V$, and of the same direction, the picture of the streamlines (and of the flow in general) will be quite different in the two cases, because the kinematic viscosity of water is more than ten times as small as that of air. Thus effects of viscosity, in particular the formation of whirls, are of much less consequence in water than in air. On the other hand, since the density of water is almost a thousand times that of air, the *force* on a solid body in a stream of water is much larger than in a stream of air. It is the object of the following sections to put these qualitative statements on a quantitative basis.

## 7.   Reynolds' Law of Similarity

It is of great importance for aerodynamic research that under certain circumstances the flow past a large body (airplane) is geometrically *similar* to the flow past a small model of similar shape.

Similarity of flow means that the flow pattern surrounding a large object is a simple enlargement of the flow pattern surrounding a small model (see Figs. 5a and 5b). The rate of linear magnification is $l_1/l_2$, where $l_1$ and $l_2$ are any two corresponding lengths of object and model, i.e., two diameters, or two circumferences, etc. The ratio $l_1/l_2$ is independent of the special choice of the characteristic length, $l$.

Similarity of flow prevails if the *directions* of the flow in any two *corresponding* points near object and model are the same. In particular, the angles $\alpha_1$ and $\alpha_2$ between flow and horizontal direction in two

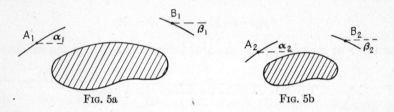

Fɪɢ. 5a        Fɪɢ. 5b

corresponding points $A_1$ and $A_2$ must be equal, and the angles $\beta_1$ and $\beta_2$ in two corresponding points $B_1$ and $B_2$ must also be equal, and so forth.

Object and model may be tested under different wind velocities, $V_1$ and $V_2$, under different pressures, $p_1$ and $p_2$, and hence under different kinematic viscosities, $\nu_1$ and $\nu_2$. Nevertheless, it has been found as a general law of physics that the two flows are similar if the two dimensionless ratios $l_1V_1/\nu_1$ and $l_2V_2/\nu_2$ have the same numerical value. These ratios are called the *Reynolds numbers*, $R_1$ and $R_2$, of object and model. *Reynolds' law of similarity* states that similarity of flow past object and model prevails if the two Reynolds numbers are equal:

$$R_1 = R_2, \text{ that is, } l_1V_1/\nu_1 = l_2V_2/\nu_2.$$

A proof of Reynolds' law based on general considerations about dimensions may be obtained as follows.

Consider an object at rest in a fluid moving with horizontal velocity $V$. The direction of the flow at a point $A$ near the object may be measured by the angle $\alpha$ of deviation from the horizontal; $\alpha$ depends on the vector distance, $d$, of the point $A$ from the center of the object; on the linear size, $l$, of the object; on the velocity, $V$; and on the kinematic viscosity, $\nu$, of the fluid. However, since $\alpha$ is a dimensionless quantity, it can depend only on the dimensionless ratios $lV/\nu$ and $dV/\nu$; that is, $\alpha$ is a function, $F(lV/\nu, dV/\nu)$, of the two ratios.

Suppose now that we consider a contraction of the size of the object from $l_1$ to $l_2$, and a contraction of the vector distance from $d_1$ to $d_2$ of the observa-

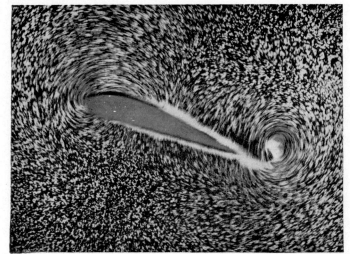

Starting Vortex

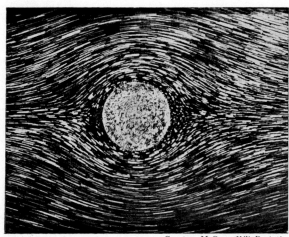

Flow round cylinder.   $V d/\nu = 0.25$

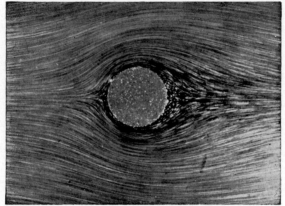

$$Vd/\nu = 1.5$$

$$Vd/\nu = 9$$

tion point $A$ at the fixed ratio $l_1/d_1 = l_2/d_2$, representing a geometrically *similar* change as in Fig. 5. If only similar changes are taken into account, $\alpha$ may be considered as a function of $lV/\nu$ alone, since the value $dV/\nu$ is determined by $lV/\nu$ and the fixed ratio $l/d$. For geometrically similar changes we thus have $\alpha = f(lV/\nu)$. In particular at the beginning and end of a similar contraction we have $\alpha_1 = f(l_1V/\nu)$ and $\alpha_2 = f(l_2V/\nu)$ as angles of flow in the two similar points $A_1$ and $A_2$ near object and model, respectively.

If we now suppose that the flows in $A_1$ and $A_2$ have the same direction, $\alpha_1 = \alpha_2$, at the same time admitting that $V$ and $\nu$ are different in the two cases, we arrive at the condition

$$f(l_1V_1/\nu_1) = \alpha_1 = \alpha_2 = f(l_2V_2/\nu_2).$$

The same consideration applied to another pair of similar points, $B_1$ and $B_2$, yields

$$g(l_1V_1/\nu_1) = \beta_1 = \beta_2 = g(l_2V_2/\nu_2),$$

etc. All these equations for similar points $A_1A_2$, $B_1B_2$, $C_1C_2$, etc., hold simultaneously only if $l_1V_1/\nu_1 = l_2V_2/\nu_2$. Similarity of flow past similar objects is thus granted if the Reynolds numbers in the two cases are the same, *i.e.*, $R_1 = R_2$.

As an example, take the case of a model $1/20$ the size of the object so that $l_1/l_2 = 20$. Both are to be tested in air, $(\mu_1 = \mu_2)$ but at different pressures, so that the kinematic viscosities $\nu = \mu/\rho$, are different. Reynolds' equation of similarity, $\rho_1 l_1 V_1/\mu_1 = \rho_2 l_2 V_2/\mu_2$ then reduces to $\rho_1 20 V_1 = \rho_2 V_2$, or since the density is proportional to the pressure, $20 p_1 V_1 = p_2 V_2$. Similarity of flow is granted when

$$
\begin{array}{ccc}
V_2 = V_1 & V_2 = 2V_1 & V_2 = 4V_1 \\
\text{or} & \text{or} & \text{etc.} \\
p_2 = 20p_1 & p_2 = 10p_1 & p_2 = 5p_1
\end{array}
$$

In general, in order to obtain similarity of flow past a small model plane, one has to apply higher wind-tunnel velocities and greater pressures than in case of a large airplane in actual flight. For this reason, wind tunnels are built for very high wind velocities and several atmospheres of pressure.

When a certain object is put into a fluid of kinematic viscosity $\nu$ and velocity $V$, the value of the Reynolds number, $R = lV/\nu$, is never defined uniquely, since $l$ might be chosen at will either as circumference, diameter, or any other characteristic length. A wing of chord $c = 5$ ft and span $b = 35$ ft travelling through air of kinematic viscosity $\nu = 0.000158$ with $V = 100$ miles/hr has Reynolds number $R \approx 4,500,000$ if the *chord* is chosen as significant length. $R$ would be seven times as large if one should identify $l$ with the span. However, this indefiniteness does not affect Reynolds' law of similarity as applied to wing and wing model. Indeed, similarity of flow is granted if $c_1 V_1/\nu_1 = c_2 V_2/\nu_2$, and this equation is not changed if multiplied on both sides by a common factor. In the case of *wings* it is customary to refer Reynolds' number to the *chord* as significant linear dimension, so that $R = cV/\nu$.

### Problems

(1) Find the Reynolds number of a wing of chord 8 ft travelling at 60 miles/hr; at 120 miles/hr.

(2) How large is the chord of a wing travelling at 100 miles/hr when the Reynolds number is 1,000,000?

(3) A model 1/15 the size of a wing is tested in a tunnel wind of 80 miles/hr at an air pressure of 6 atm. What is the speed of the corresponding real wing? Also find the suction on a part of the upper surface of the real wing, if the suction at the corresponding part of the model is found to be $\frac{1}{2}$ atm.

(4) The flow past a wing travelling at 150 miles/hr is to be tested on a model of size 1/5. The tunnel wind may have a velocity half that of sound ($= \frac{1}{2}$ 1080 ft/sec). What tunnel pressure is needed?

## 8. Boundary Layer; Laminar and Turbulent Flow

The Reynolds number plays a decisive part in determining the transition from *laminar* to *turbulent flow*. When a fluid is passed through a glass tube with moderate velocity, all fluid particles travel parallel to the *axis* of the tube, although with different velocities. The velocity has a maximum on the axis itself, and gradually decreases toward the walls, where it is zero because of adhesion. The flow then may be divided into concentric cylindrical layers or "lamellae" representing "laminar flow."

If, however, the velocity $V$ on the axis is increased too much, the particles in the tube begin to move irregularly, not only parallel to the axis but also toward and from the wall in a "turbulent" manner. This transformation may be observed through the glass walls, especially when the fluid contains dust particles. Turbulence begins to appear as soon as the Reynolds number, $R = rV/\nu$, in a tube of radius $r$ attains a certain critical value, $R_{\text{crit}}$. Experience shows that the *critical Reynolds number* determining the transformation from laminar to turbulent flow is of order 500,000. The critical $R$ also depends on the smoothness of the walls and, in the case of short tubes, on the length of the tube, since turbulence develops only some distance from the entrance of the tube.

A wing ought to be constructed so as to avoid turbulent flow along its surface as far as possible. This is achieved by *streamlining*. If the velocity $V$, or rather the Reynolds number, $R = cV/v$ with $c$ = chord, is increased too much, the resulting turbulence will increase the drag and decrease the lift of the wing to a considerable extent.

The conflict between streamline pattern and adhesion leads to the formation of a transition layer or *boundary layer* of air on the surface of the solid body. Within this layer one has a gradual transition from $v = 0$ on the surface itself, into the velocity, $v$, as required by the streamline pattern. The thickness, $\delta$, of this transition layer varies along the surface of the body. At the front stagnation point, where both adhesion and streamline pattern agree to produce a velocity $v = 0$, the boundary layer has thickness zero. Going along the surface to a distance, $l$, from the stagnation point, the conflict between streamline flow and adhesion grows, and the thickness of the transition layer increases according to the approximate formula

$$\delta = l\sqrt{1/R} = \sqrt{lv/V}.$$

That is, the thickness increases with increasing distance, $l$, from the stagnation point, with increasing kinematic viscosity, but decreases with increasing speed, $V$. The boundary layer surrounding a wing is the source of turbulence and air circulation (vorticity), which in their turn are responsible for the wind force on the wing. Without adhesion and viscosity an airfoil would suffer neither lift nor drag.

The cross-section of a wing with its blunt leading and sharp trailing edge is so designed as to reduce the turbulence along the lower surface to a negligible amount. If the flow could also be kept laminar along the upper surface, the drag would be decreased, and the suction upon the upper surface would become more uniformly distributed, instead of acting chiefly on the forward part of the wing. It has been proposed, therefore, to cover the upper wing surface with an endless ribbon emerging from the leading edge and re-entering the hollow of the wing at the trailing edge. If the ribbon could be drawn over the surface with approximately the same velocity as the relative wind, the conflict between adhesion and streamline flow would disappear, and turbulence could be reduced to a minimum. Unfortunately this idea cannot be put into practice. A variant of it, however, has met with some success in the form of the rotor ship (section 22).

The thickness of the boundary layer cannot be defined exactly. All one can say is that there is a *gradual* transition from $v = 0$ on the boundary itself to the streamline velocity farther outside. The transition is practically completed within a width $\delta = l\sqrt{1/R}$. The thickness of the transition layer is comparatively small under ordinary circumstances. Near the rear edge of a wing of chord length 5 feet ($l = 5$) one obtains

$$\delta = l\sqrt{1/R} = 5/\sqrt{4,500,000} = 0.002 \text{ ft.}$$

when assuming the same Reynolds number, as in the example of section 7. In spite of the small width, $\delta$, the boundary layer is of great consequence as the seat of shearing forces near the wing surface. These forces lead to a small whirl whose intensity increases until it disengages itself from the wing and makes room for a new process of whirl formation, and so forth. The whirls produced by, and left in the wake of, the wing are the chief source of the drag. For details see Chapter III.

# Chapter II

## The Profile of the Wing

### 9. Description of an Airplane

We begin with a description of an airplane and its principal parts.

(1) The *wings* support the airplane in the air. They consist of curved planes fastened to both sides of the body either in high-wing, mid-wing, or low-wing position. Wings attached above the body on a superstructure are called parasol wings.

(2) The *fuselage*, or body, of the airplane carries the crew, cargo, and passengers.

(3) The *engine-propeller set* supplies the forward thrust to the airplane. The *engine* is mounted either within the fuselage or, in the case of twin-engined, tri-motored, etc. planes, in front of the wing in *nacelles*. The *propeller* is an airscrew with two or three blades revolving at high speed, up to 1800 revolutions per minute.

(4) The *control surfaces* are the elevator, the rudder, and the ailerons. The *elevator* is a movable part of the horizontal tail surface and may be turned up and down so as to control climbing and diving; it also stabilizes the airplane in level flight. The *rudder* is a part of the vertical tail surface, or fin, and may be moved to the right and left; it exerts directional control and stabilizes the plane on a straight course. The *ailerons* are flaps hinged to the rear edge of the wings. They are connected through a control stick so that one movement of the latter turns one aileron upward and the other one downward so as to produce banking.

(5) The *landing gear* or undercarriage consists of rubber-tired wheels supporting the airplane on the ground. The landing gear is withdrawn into the fuselage during flight to reduce air resistance. Some airplanes have skiis for landing on snow. Seaplanes carry floats or pontoons for landing on water.

### 10. The Wing

The contour of a wing viewed from above or spotted from below is called the *planform*. The first airplanes had wings of straight

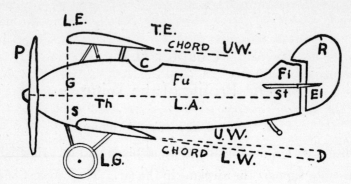

FIG. 6

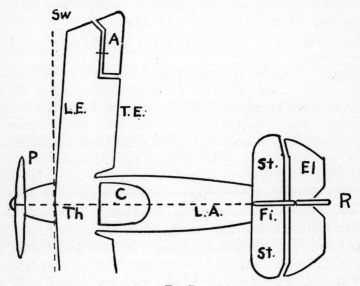

FIG. 7

| | | | |
|---|---|---|---|
| A | Aileron | L.G. | Landing Gear |
| C | Cockpit | L.W. | Lower Wing |
| Ch | Chord | P | Propeller |
| D | Decalage | R | Rudder |
| El | Elevator | S | Stagger |
| Fi | Fin | St | Stabilizer |
| Fu | Fuselage | Sw | Sweepback Angle |
| G | Gap | T.E. | Trailing Edge |
| L.A. | Longit. Axis | Th | Thrust Line |
| L.E. | Leading Edge | U.W. | Upper Wing |

rectangular planform; they were inexpensive and easy to construct but gave a poor performance in flight. The present streamlined wing or "airfoil" yields a better windforce distribution with increased stability, reduced drag, and larger lift. Fig. 8a shows the planform of a *tapered* wing. Fig. 8b illustrates positive and negative *rake*. Fig. 8c shows a wing with *sweepback*. When the wing tips are higher than the root, the angle between right and left wing is known as the *dihedral angle*. The opposite case of wings angling down is classified as *anhedral*. Dihedral at the root and anhedral farther out gives a *gull-*

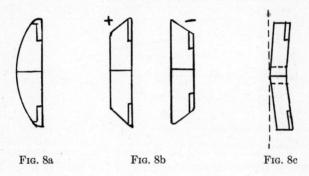

FIG. 8a          FIG. 8b          FIG. 8c

*shaped* wing; the opposite arrangement produces inverted gull-shape. Wings are sometimes given a slight *twist* so as to reduce the wing pressure near the tips.

The distance from one wing tip to the other is defined as the wing *span*, usually denoted by the letter $b$ and measured in feet. Wing spans range from 30 feet in small trainers (compare with Da Vinci's human bird (section 1), to 212 feet in the giant Douglas B-19 bomber. A vertical cross-section through the wing shows the *profile* with its blunt leading edge and sharp trailing edge. The distance from the leading to the trailing edge is defined as the wing *chord* and is denoted by the letter $c$. In the case of rectangular planform the ratio $b/c$ = span/chord is known as the *aspect ratio* (AR) of the wing. AR's range from 5 in fast pursuit planes, to 8 in heavy transport planes. If the chord varies along the span in the case of non-rectangular planforms, the AR is defined as the ratio $b^2/S$, where $S$ is the area of the wing:

$$\text{Aspect ratio (AR)} = b/c, \text{ or } b^2/S.$$

A typical wing section, or *profile*, is shown in Fig. 9, with the *chord* of length $c$ between leading and trailing edge. Halfway between the upper and lower surface of the wing runs the *mean camber line* (line in Fig. 9), usually of parabolic shape. The *thickness* of the wing is measured at right angles to the mean camber line. Maximum cam-ber is usually located at 30 per cent from the leading edge. The ex-traordinary lifting power of cambered wings as compared with flat boards is one of the most gratifying results of aerodynamic research.

The angle between chord and relative wind is the *angle of attack, $\alpha$,* of the wing. The angle between the propeller axis or direction of thrust and relative wind is known as the *angle of incidence*. The lift of the wing increases with increasing $\alpha$ up to a certain maximum value, above which the lift decreases again.

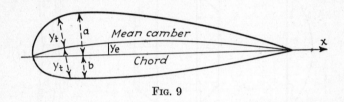

F<small>IG</small>. 9

Wing profiles are denoted by 4-index symbols, like (6315). This symbol means: The maximum camber of the wing is 6 per cent of the chord; it is located at 3 tenths of $c$ (or 30 per cent) from the leading edge, the maximum thickness is 15 per cent of $c$. A number of profiles with their 4-digit symbols are shown in Fig. 10. If the second digit (3 tenths) is replaced by two digits (30 per cent) one arrives at the 5-digit symbols used lately in the reports of the N.A.C.A., *i.e.,* National Advisory Committee for Aeronautics.

A wing section may also be characterized by the maximum upper camber, *a,* above the chord and the maximum lower camber below the chord (Fig. 9). The upper camber is always positive, whereas the lower camber may be "positive," to produce a convex-concave wing, or "negative," yielding a double convex wing.

### 11.   Wind Force on a Flat Plate

When air is blown with velocity $V$ at right angles toward a flat plate of area, $S$, or when the plate moves with velocity $V$ across still air, a complicated process of air deflection takes place near the sharp edges, followed by eddy formation behind the plate. This process may be described inaccurately by saying that a certain amount of air is "stopped" every second by the area $S$. The air stopped per second is contained in a column of length $V$, cross-section $S$, and volume $V \times S$. The mass of this air is $V \times S \times \rho$, and its momentum is $V$ times the mass, that is, $\rho \times V^2 \times S$, where $\rho$ is the density or mass per unit of volume.

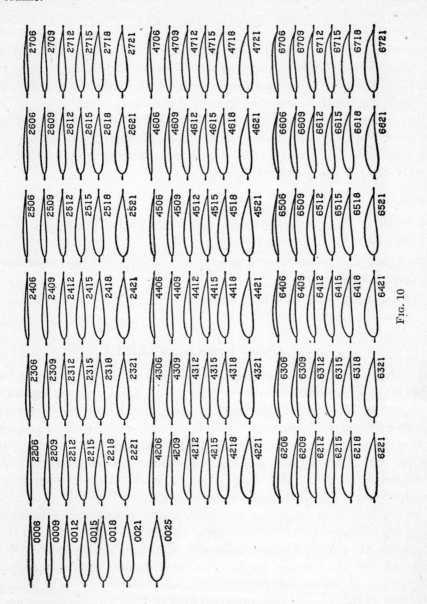

Fig. 10

According to Newton's second law of motion, the force $F$ on the plate should be equal to the momentum stopped by the plate per unit of time, that is, $F = \rho V^2 S$. In fact, the air is not completely stopped by the plate, so that the force is less than $\rho V^2 S$—how much less may be found by actual experiments only. Experience shows that the actual force is only about 64 per cent of the former value, that is,

$$F = 0.64\rho V^2 S = 1.28(\tfrac{1}{2}\rho V^2)S.$$

The constant 1.28 is called the *force coefficient* of the plate for perpendicular incidence of the wind. When $V$ is measured in ft/sec, $S$ in ft², and $\rho$ in lbs/ft³, $F$ is obtained in poundals. If $F$ must be obtained in pounds, the density $\rho$ must be measured in slugs.

The *force coefficient*, $C$, is defined as the factor of $\tfrac{1}{2}\rho V^2 S$ (in the case of a flat plate, $C$ equals 1.28). This is the American definition applied in this book. In Great Britain the force coefficient is defined as the factor of $\rho V^2 S$ (in the present case, $C = 0.64$).

### Problems

(1) A sail of area 25 ft² is set at right angles to a wind of 15 miles/hr. How large is the wind force in pounds?

(2) A glass window can stand a pressure of 30 lbs/ft². Find the wind speed which will break it.

(3) How strong is the wind force against a vertical 1.5 × 3-foot windshield of a car driven at 30 or 60 miles/hr?

## 12.   Wind Force on an Airfoil

When a thin *plate* is presented to an airstream at an oblique angle, the air is compelled to rush at high speed around the sharp edge (Fig. 2b). Eventually this leads to the formation of whirls accompanied by a large increase in the wind resistance. An *airfoil*, on the other hand, divides the incoming airflow smoothly in two parts; the upper part is accelerated and the lower part retarded by the curved (cambered) profile. This distribution (Fig. 3b) yields suction above and excess pressure below the wing, according to Bernoulli's theorem. Near the trailing edge the accelerated and decelerated airstreams join with almost equal velocities and almost equal pressures, so that there is only a small pressure difference which might give rise to a flow around the sharp edge itself. The wing profile thus reduces the formation of whirls and produces lift accompanied by only a small amount of drag. The lift/drag ratio may be boosted as far as 20 to 1, compared to the ratio of 6 to 1 in the case of a flat plate under the most favorable angle of attack between wind direction and chord. Efficient long-distance flight became possible only with the introduction of the streamlined cambered wing.

When an airfoil of area $S$ is exposed to a steady wind of velocity $V$, the wind force is controlled by a similar formula as in the case of a flat plate. The wind force is proportional to the density $\rho$, to the plate area $S$, and to the square of the velocity, that is,

$$F = C(\tfrac{1}{2}\rho V^2)S$$

where $C$ is a factor of proportionality, called *force coefficient*, whose value depends

(a) on the *angle* between chord and wind ( = angle of attack $\alpha$);
(b) on the *shape* of the wing, but not on its size;
(c) to a small degree also on the *Reynolds number*, $R = cV/\nu$.

The wind force, $F$, may be decomposed into a *drag* component parallel to the relative wind, and a *lift* component at right angles to the relative wind. Lift and drag are always perpendicular to each other.

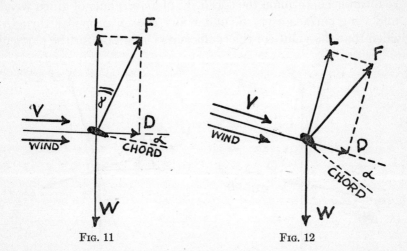

Fig. 11          Fig. 12

However, the lift points straight upward only in the case of horizontal flight where the wind is horizontal. The decomposition of the wind force in two perpendicular components is shown for level flight in Fig. 11, for climb in Fig. 12, and for dive in Fig. 13. In all three cases it is assumed that the airplane travels to the left so that the relative wind points to the right. Under equal conditions (a) (b) (c) and at equal wind speeds and air densities, the force diagrams of Figs. 12 and 13 are obtained by tilting Fig. 11 up or down through a certain angle. However, since the force of gravity (weight) always points downward, the vector composition of wind force, thrust, and gravity yields three different force diagrams (compare with Fig. 14).

The angle between the total wind force, $F$, and its lift component, $L$, may be denoted by the letter $\delta$. $F$ then divides into two components, $L = F \cos \delta$, and $D = F \sin \delta$; thus one arrives at the following formulas for lift and drag:

$$\text{lift } L = C_L(\tfrac{1}{2}\rho V^2)S, \qquad\qquad \text{where } C_L = C \cos \delta,$$
$$\text{drag } D = C_D(\tfrac{1}{2}\rho V^2)S, \qquad\qquad \text{where } C_D = C \sin \delta.$$

The inversion of these formulas yields $V$ expressed in terms of the *lift coefficient*, $C_L$, and the *drag coefficient*, $C_D$, respectively:

$$V = \sqrt{L/\tfrac{1}{2}\rho S C_L}, \qquad\qquad V = \sqrt{D/\tfrac{1}{2}\rho S C_D}.$$

In level flight the lift balances the weight, $L = W$, and the drag is overcome by the propeller thrust, $D = T$, so that one has

$$V = \sqrt{W/\tfrac{1}{2}\rho S C_L}, \qquad\qquad V = \sqrt{T/\tfrac{1}{2}\rho S C_D} \text{ (level flight)}.$$

These formulas determine the speed, $V$, of an airplane of given weight, $W$, and wing surface area, $S$, under any chosen propeller thrust, $T$, provided that the values of the coefficients $C_L$ and $C_D$ for the particular

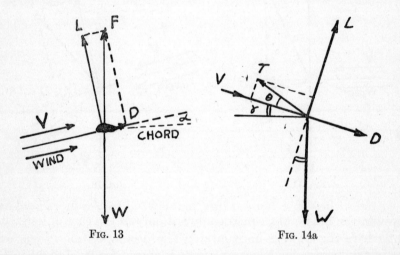

Fig. 13                                     Fig. 14a

wing shape are known. $C_L$ and $C_D$ depend on the angle of attack, $\alpha$. If $\rho$ is given in lbs/ft³, then $F$, $L$, and $D$ are obtained in poundals. If $\rho$ is given in slugs, then $F$, $L$, and $D$ are obtained in pounds, always supposing that $S$ is measured in ft² and $V$ in ft/sec.

The values of $C_L$ and $C_D$ as well as the ratio $C_L/C_D$ may be plotted as ordinates against $\alpha$ as abscissa. The *characteristic curves* (see Fig. 15) obtained in this way for a certain wing *shape* are valid for all sizes, and may therefore be obtained from wind-tunnel experiments with small models of similar shape. The characteristic curves change very little with the Reynolds number, $R$. They are usually plotted for a certain intermediary value of $R$.

### 13. Equilibrium of Forces

The wing is in equilibrium when the total force as well as the total torque ( = moment of force) vanishes. The wind force, $F$, with its components $L$ and $D$, thus has to balance the force of gravity, represented by the weight, $W$, of the airplane, and the propeller thrust, $T$, parallel to the longitudinal axis of the airplane. The same is true for the torques of $F$, $W$, and $T$.

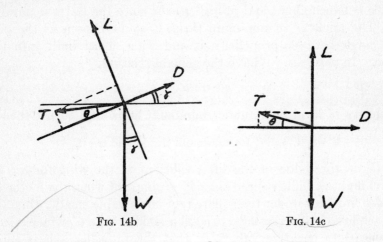

FIG. 14b          FIG. 14c

The angle between relative wind, $V$, and horizontal may be called $\gamma$; $\gamma$ is the angle of ascent during a climb, and is the gliding angle in downward flight. The angle between wind and thrust is $\Theta$. The force components at right angles to the wind must cancel each other, and so must the force components parallel to the wind. These two requirements lead to the following equations:

(1) Climb: $L + T \sin \Theta = W \cos \gamma$
$D + W \sin \gamma = T \cos \Theta$   (Fig. 14a)

(2) Power Dive: $L + T \sin \Theta = W \cos \gamma$
$D - W \sin \gamma = T \cos \Theta$   (Fig. 14b)

(3) Glide ($T = 0$): $L = W \cos \gamma$
$D = W \sin \gamma$

(4) Level flight ($\gamma = 0$): $L + T \sin \Theta = W$
$D = T \cos \Theta$   (Fig. 14c)

(5) Level flight with horizontal thrust ($\gamma = 0$, $\Theta = 0$): $L = W$,
$D = T$.

Similar equations also apply to the airplane as a whole, with the slight modification that $D$ has to include the drag of other parts of the airplane, and that $L$ includes the lift contribution of the tail which sometimes appears as a negative contribution, or *tail load.*

Let us discuss case (5) first.   In level flight with horizontal propeller axis, the horizontal drag is counteracted by the thrust, and the vertical lift by the weight.   The ratio $L/D$ equals $W/T$ in this case.   On the other hand, $L/D$ depends on the angle of attack; $\alpha$ could be chosen so as to yield a maximum value of $L/D$, and hence a *minimum value of thrust, T,* required to support the weight.   This particular angle of attack may be called $\alpha'$.   In horizontal flight the same angle $\alpha'$ is also the angle between chord and propeller axis, since the latter is parallel to $V$.   The angle $\alpha'$ of minimum thrust may be chosen as the permanent angle between propeller axis and wing chord built into the airplane.   In this case we have the general relation:

$$\alpha = \theta + \alpha'.$$

The velocity of level flight under minimum horizontal thrust then is

$$V' = \sqrt{W/\tfrac{1}{2}\rho S C'_L} \text{ for minimum thrust and } \theta = 0,$$

where $C'_L$ is the value of the lift coefficient of the wing for $\alpha = \alpha'$.

Level flight at higher speed than $V'$ is obtained when the factor $C_L$ in the denominator under the square root has a value smaller than $C'_L$. This is achieved by decreasing $\alpha$ to a value smaller than $\alpha'$, which means decreasing $\theta$ to negative values, so that the propeller axis is tilted downward slightly.   At the same time one does not have minimum thrust any more, which means that the engine must be speeded up. This is the general case (4).

During a glide, as in case (3) the ratio $L/D$ equals $\cos\gamma/\sin\gamma$, which is the cotangent of the gliding angle $\gamma$.   The same ratio $L/D$, on the other hand, depends on the angle $\alpha$.   Thus $\gamma$ and $\alpha$ are mutually dependent so that a chosen gliding angle, $\gamma$, is achieved only under a certain corresponding angle $\alpha$.   The gliding speed, too, is determined by the gliding angle.   Indeed, $V$ is obtained in case (3) by substituting in the formula

$$V = \sqrt{L/\tfrac{1}{2}\rho S C_L}$$

for $L$ the value $W\cos\gamma$, and for $C_L$ the value belonging to the angle $\alpha$ associated with $\gamma$.   Thus, both $\alpha$ and $V$ are determined by the chosen gliding angle $\gamma$.

Turning to cases (1) and (2), the speed $V$ of the dive (climb) and the angle of descent (ascent), $\gamma$, are determined by the angle of attack and the thrust, and *vice versa*. Indeed, for given weight of the airplane, case (1) as well as case (2) is characterized by two equations between the four variables $\alpha$, $\gamma$, $T$, and $V$, so that two variables determine the other two.

When landing, the airplane must go into level flight with power off ($T=0$ and $\gamma=0$), and with a minimum *landing speed*. In order to obtain small velocity, $V = \sqrt{W/\tfrac{1}{2}\rho SC_L}$, one has to choose the angle $\alpha$ of attack so that $C_L$ has maximum value.

The *rate of work* of the propeller thrust in level flight (case 5) is the product of force and distance per second:

$$\text{rate of work} = T \times V = D \times V = C_D(\tfrac{1}{2}\rho V^2)V.$$

If $V$ in this expression is replaced by $V = \sqrt{W/\tfrac{1}{2}\rho SC_L}$, one obtains the formula

$$\text{rate of work} = (C_D/C_L^{3/2})(W^3/\tfrac{1}{2}\rho S)^{1/2}.$$

which has a certain practical significance for finding the rate of work in level flight for any angle of attack (which in its turn determines $V$, $C_D$, and $C_L$) when the weight of the plane and the wing area are given.

*Example 1:* What is the landing speed of a 1000-lb airplane of wing area 80 ft² with a maximum value $C_L = 1.3$?

*Solution:*  $V = \sqrt{W/\tfrac{1}{2}\rho SC_L}$
$$= (1{,}000/\tfrac{1}{2} \times 0.002378 \times 80 \times 1.3)^{1/2} = 28.3 \text{ ft/sec.}$$

*Example 2:* An airplane of wing area 120 ft² flies at 144 ft/sec under an angle of attack which belongs to a drag coefficient $C_D = 0.04$. What is the rate of work?

*Solution:*  Rate of work $= C_D \times \tfrac{1}{2}\rho SV^3 = 0.04 \times \tfrac{1}{2} \times 0.002378 \times 144^3/550$
$$= 2{,}600 \text{ hp.}$$

## 14.  Center of Pressure

The total wind force, $F$, on an airfoil is the vector sum of the many small forces, $f$, which act on the numerous small parts of the wing surface. Let us consider a wing of large aspect ratio, $b/c$, and of rectangular planform so as to yield two-dimensional flow (except near the wing tips). If the wing span amounts to $n$ feet, it may then be divided into $n$ segments, each of span 1 ft, and each having the same cross-section (profile). The wind force is the same on each segment, and the direction of the force is in the plane of the cross-section. One therefore may consider the force distribution over one segment of span 1 ft, that is, the force per unit length of span. The force distribution may be illustrated by a wing profile spiked with arrows indicating the magnitude and direction of the wind force per unit length of span and per unit length of circumference of the profile, as exemplified in Figs. 4a and 4b.

Let us select an arbitrary point, $P$, somewhere on the *chord* of the wing profile. The total moment of force (torque) about $P$ is the resultant of the many small torques supplied by the small forces on the line elements of the circumference. There is one particular point on the chord, however, about which the resulting torque vanishes. This point on the chord is called the *center of pressure* (c.p.) of the wind force. Its position depends on the orientation of the wing, that is, on the angle of attack. The wind force, $F$, as a whole may be thought to attack at the c.p. without producing torque, just as gravity may be thought to attack at the center of gravity (c.g.) without producing torque.

The position of the c.p. "travels" along the chord when the angle of attack, $\alpha$, is changed. At small $\alpha$, the c.p. is located near the rear end (trailing edge) of the wing. That is, when holding the wing near the trailing edge, the wind force would not upset the balance. When $\alpha$ is increased, the c.p. travels forward along the chord. That is, when the wing is nosed up one has to support it at a point farther forward in order to keep it in balance under the wind force. If one did *not* shift the place of support when increasing $\alpha$, the wind would produce a torque tending to increase $\alpha$ still further, resulting in a cumulative increase of $\alpha$. This is called *unstable travel* of the c.p. Although the wing itself usually has this characteristic, the airplane as a whole is stabilized against cumulative $\alpha$-increase by the counter-torque of the horizontal tail surface.

When the wing is pitched up gradually the c.p. reaches its *maximum forward position* at a certain definite angle of attack. A further increase of $\alpha$ would produce backward travel of the c.p.

The c.p. at a certain angle of attack was defined as the point about which the wind torque vanishes. The torque about other points of the chord at the same $\alpha$, does not vanish. Of particular interest is the torque about the leading edge of the wing, called *pitching moment*, and denoted by the letter $M$. The value of $M$ depends on $\alpha$. The pitching moment is proportional to the chord length, $c$, (which serves as *lever arm*) and to the product $\rho V^2 S$ (which is proportional to the wind *force* on the wing). Altogether the pitching moment is

$$M = C_M(\tfrac{1}{2}\rho V^2)Sc$$

with a factor of proportionality, $C_M$, known as the *pitching coefficient*. $C_M$ depends on the shape (not size) of the profile, on the Reynolds number $R = cV/\nu$, and on the angle of attack.

The moment is considered positive when it tends to increase the angle of attack. According to this definition, the pitching moment of a wing is always negative, since the wind tends to lift the trailing edge, the leading edge being the axis. Balance of torque is achieved by installing the horizontal tail surface in a slightly nosed down position, so as to yield a small *tail load*.

## 15. Characteristic Curves

Before deriving the aerodynamic qualities of a given wing profile, it is necessary to know the values of $C_L$ and $C_D$ at various angles of attack and for a variety of Reynolds numbers. Determinations of the two coefficients may be carried out in a wind tunnel with a small model. Fortunately both coefficients are almost constant, for any chosen $\alpha$, over a wide range of Reynolds numbers.

The values of the lift and drag coefficients of a certain standard wing profile are plotted for a variety of angles of attack in Fig. 15. The same diagram also contains curves for the lift/drag ratio, $L/D = C_L/C_D$, and for the position of the c.p. in percentage of the chord; all curves are plotted against the angle $\alpha$ as abscissa, yielding *four characteristic curves* altogether. If one wants to calculate the lift and drag of a certain wing (for example, the standard wing whose characteristic curves are plotted in Fig. 15) for any angle of attack, one may look up the corresponding values of $C_L$ and $C_D$ on the diagram and substitute them in the formulas

$$L = C_L(\tfrac{1}{2}\rho V^2)S \quad \text{and} \quad D = C_D(\tfrac{1}{2}\rho V^2)S.$$

The same diagram also allows calculation of the wind torque about any point on the wing profile, simply by multiplying the wind force $F$ (the resultant of $L$ and $D$) by the distance of the point from the line of action defined as the line parallel to $F$ through the c.p.

The characteristic curves reveal the following features of a wing.

$(C_L)$ The lift coefficient is positive for small negative angles, *e.g.*, $\alpha = -2°$. When $\alpha$ is increased to positive values, $C_L$ increases until maximum $C_L$ is reached at $\alpha = 22°$. For higher angles of attack the lift coefficient decreases rapidly; 22° is the *stalling angle* of the wing.

$(C_D)$ Beginning at negative angles, *e.g.*, $\alpha = -4°$, the drag coefficient, $C_D$, decreases with increasing $\alpha$ until minimum $C_D$ is reached at about $\alpha = 0$. Further increase of $\alpha$ leads to ever-increasing drag coefficient.

($L/D$) The two curves for $C_L$ and $C_D$ together determine the curve for $L/D = C_L/C_D$. Although the lift coefficient has its maximum at the stalling angle of 22°, maximum $L/D$ is found at $\alpha = 3°$ due to the rapid increase of $C_D$ with increasing $\alpha$.

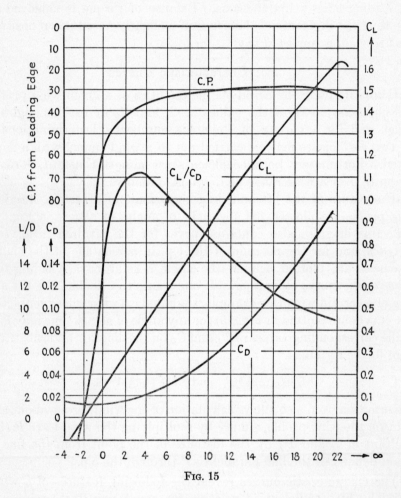

FIG. 15

(C.P.) The distance of the center of pressure from the leading edge is plotted in percentage of the chord $c$. At $\alpha = -1°$ the c.p. is found at 85 per cent from the leading edge. When $\alpha$ is increased to small positive values, the c.p. travels forward rapidly. At 10° it is found at 30 per cent from the leading edge, where it remains rather stable when $\alpha$ increases to the stalling angle of 22°.

It is customary also to plot a curve for the coefficient $C_M$ of the pitching moment for various angles $\alpha$ as a fifth characteristic. The significance of these curves for the stability and performance of the airplane in flight will be discussed in Chapters IV and V.

## 16. Correction for Aspect Ratio

The characteristic curves for $C_L$, $C_D$, and for the ratio $L/D$ depend on the shape (not size) of the wing profile, and to a certain degree also on the span/chord ratio (aspect ratio, AR). It would be necessary therefore, to test various wing profile models not only at various angles of attack but also for various aspect ratios. That is, after deciding on a certain profile, one would have to determine $C_L$ and $C_D$ with models whose aspect ratio ranged from 3 to 8, each of them for many different angles $\alpha$. Fortunately this experimental work may be greatly reduced by virtue of a general rule, according to which the C-curves for any AR may be derived after the curves have been measured for one particular AR only. Let us assume that the $C_L$ values of a certain profile shape have been measured on a model of standard AR = 6. In order to obtain the $C_L$ values for AR = 8 one has to multiply the standard $C_L$ values by the common factor 1.07, so that the standard $C_L$ curve is to be enlarged at the rate of 1.07 to 1 in the direction of the ordinate axis, without changing the $\alpha$-scale along the abscissa. The $C_L$ curve for AR = 3, on the other hand, is obtained by contracting the standard ordinates at the ratio of 0.82 to 1. The *correction factors* for $C_L$ from AR = 3 to 8 are given in Table 5. The curve for AR = 6 does not need correction; its correction factor is 1.

Table 5.   Correction Factors

| Aspect Ratio | 3 | 4 | 5 | 6 | 7 | 8 |
|---|---|---|---|---|---|---|
| $C_L$ correction | 0.82 | 0.89 | 0.95 | 1.00 | 1.04 | 1.07 |
| $L/D$ correction | 0.7 | 0.8 | 0.91 | 1.00 | 1.08 | 1.16 |

The table is valid for all angles of attack, that is, for the whole $C_L$ curve at once. *The same table applies to all profiles and all angles of attack.* The $C_L$ curve for any profile and any aspect ratio is obtained from the $C_L$ curve of the same profile shape measured at AR = 6 by a simple enlargement in the direction of the ordinate axis.

Exactly the same has been found to apply to the $C_D$ curves, except that the correction factors are different from those for $C_L$. The ratio of the correction factors for $C_L$ and $C_D$ represents the correction factors for $C_L/C_D$, that is, for the $L/D$ curve. They are found in the bottom row of Table 5. For example, when the $L/D$ curve has been determined experimentally for standard AR = 6, the $L/D$ curve of the same profile shape for AR = 3 is obtained by contracting all ordinates by the ratio of 0.7 to 1. A huge amount of experimental work is saved in this way. Of course, one first had to determine the correction factors of Table 5 for various AR's by wind tunnel experiments, and later it was found that the factors were the same for different profile shapes and different angles of attack.

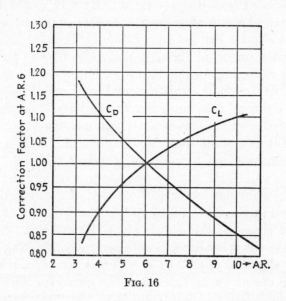

Fig. 16

The two rows of Table 5 are represented as two curves in Fig. 16 with the AR as abscissa. It is quite significant that both curves ascend with increasing AR. This means that $C_L$ as well as $L/D$ becomes larger with increasing AR, making it desirable to use large AR's.

### 17. Selection of Airfoils

The aerodynamic properties of an airfoil depend on the profile (cross-section) and planform (top view). The planform ought to have large AR in order to yield large $C_L$ and $L/D$ values. For practical reasons of construction, however, the AR is always kept below 8.

We now turn to the discussion of several features of a wing which may be derived from the characteristic curves.

(a) **Effectiveness.** The work of flying an airplane over a given distance is the product of the distance and the force of drag which must be overcome by the propeller thrust. Maximum economy or effectiveness, that is, minimum work, is obtained when the drag has minimum value, at a time when the lift is equal to the weight of the airplane. From the equation $L/D = C_L/C_D$ we obtain $D = L/(C_L/C_D)$ $= W/(C_L/C_D)$; therefore

$$D = \text{minimum for } C_L/C_D = \text{maximum.}$$

That is, maximum effectiveness in level flight over a given distance is obtained at an angle of attack at which $L/D = C_L/C_D$ has maximum value. (This is the case for $\alpha = 3°$ in the example of Fig. 15.) The formula

$$V = \sqrt{W/\tfrac{1}{2}\rho S C_L}$$

then determines the speed under the aforementioned angle of attack. The most effective or economic wing shape is the one which yields the largest maximum value of $C_L/C_D$.

(b) **Speed.** The power or rate of work, $P$, the speed, $V$, and the drag, $D$, are related by the equation $V = P/D$; or, since $D = C_D(\tfrac{1}{2}\rho V^2)S$, by the equation $V = P/(\tfrac{1}{2}\rho V^2 S C_D)$. Multiplying both sides by $V^2$ and taking the cube root one obtains:

$$V = \sqrt[3]{P/\tfrac{1}{2}\rho S C_D}$$

Maximum speed of travel is obtained when the engine works at full power and when the angle of attack is chosen so that $C_D$ has minimum value ($\alpha = 0°$ in the example of Fig. 15). The speediest wing shape is that which yields the least minimum value of the drag coefficient, $C_D$.

(c) **Landing.** The landing speed is the lowest speed at which the wing is able to support the weight, $W$, of the airplane. From the formula [see (a)]:

$$V = \sqrt{W/\tfrac{1}{2}\rho S C_L}$$

one learns that minimum speed is obtained at an angle of attack at which $C_L$ has maximum value ($\alpha = 20°$ in Fig. 15). The lowest landing speed is obtained from a wing shape which has the largest maximum value of $C_L$.

(d) **Climb.** The power consumed by an airplane in level flight is $P = DV = C_D(\tfrac{1}{2}\rho V^2)SV = C_D\tfrac{1}{2}\rho SV^3$. Substituting for $V$ the value $\sqrt{W/\tfrac{1}{2}\rho S C_L}$, one obtains

$$P = \sqrt{W^3/\tfrac{1}{2}\rho S}(C_D/C_L^{2/3}).$$

Least power is consumed in level flight by using a wing shape with the least minimum value of $C_D/C_L^{2/3}$. The same wing shape is best fitted for rapid *climb* because the latter depends on the excess of maximum power available over minimum power needed for level flight.

(e) **Center of pressure.** In order to leave sufficient space for the cockpit, the wing must be located as far forward as possible. On the other hand, for reasons of stability, the c.p. must not be forward of the c.g. of the airplane. Concurrence of the two reasons advocates a wing in which the maximum forward position of the c.p. is removed as far as possible from the leading edge.

At negative angles of attack, *i.e.*, during a dive, the c.p. travels toward the trailing edge. This position yields high values for the pitching moment about the leading edge, accompanied by a large torque on the wing; this calls for a strong wing structure. It is desirable, therefore, to select a wing whose c.p. at negative angles of attack is not too close to the trailing edge.

## 18.  Distribution of Wind Load

The arrows of Figs. 4a and 4b toward and away from the wing profile represent the excess and deficiency of pressure of the air flow past the wing. Each arrow is perpendicular to the wing surface element from which it starts or on which it ends. It has one component parallel to the *chord* (tangential component) and one component perpendicular to the chord (normal component). The *normal* force components on the upper surface draw, and those on the lower surface push the wing in a direction perpendicular to the chord. The tangential force components exert a force toward the trailing edge parallel to the chord.

As seen from Figs. 4a and 4b, excess pressure and suction are large near the leading edge, and small near the trailing edge of the wing. It is for this reason that the center of pressure is found near the leading edge; it is the point on the chord about which the wind torque is zero. The resultant of push and pull per unit of wing area perpendicular to the chord is known as the *load* per unit area. The load is large near the leading edge and small near the trailing edge.

The load distribution from leading to trailing edges would be the same for every wing section along the whole span if the latter were long enough to give two-dimensional flow. Actually, the load distribution over a wing section depends on the position of the section along the span. Tapered wings have the advantage of yielding an almost constant load distribution along the whole span, whereas straight, rectangular wings have too much load near the wing tips.

## 19.  High-Altitude Flight

It has been a long time since sheepskin suits and oxygen bottles were considered as adequate protection for high-altitude flight. Today, when altitudes of more than 30,000 feet are not unusual, the pilot must be protected by a sealed cabin against cold and lack of pressure in order to keep his tissues from "boiling up."

A 1200 hp engine develops only 500 hp at 20,000 feet and 250 hp at 25,000 feet.  To maintain the engine power, air of ordinary sea-level pressure is supplied by a *supercharger*, so that the engine may "breathe" normally.  The ordinary centrifugal supercharger consists of a radial compression pump connected with the engine shaft by gears which may be shifted from low at moderate elevations to high at extreme altitudes.  The supercharger not only increases the air pressure supplied to the carburetor but provides for a more thorough mixture of the fuel with the air, resulting in a faster rate of combustion.

The *turbo-supercharger* developed by Sanford Moss uses the exhaust gases, which are emerging under a considerable excess pressure, to drive a turbine at the tremendous rate of 30,000 rpm.  In order to get rid of the great heat developed during the compression of the rarefied air, an extra cooling unit must be installed whose fans rotate at a much lower speed than the turbine itself.

A serious problem at high altitudes arises from the different heat coefficients of expansion of various materials.  Steel expands only half as much as aluminum, and leaks are inevitable when the temperature goes down to −55° C (−67° F), which is the temperature in the stratosphere above 36,000 feet.  At such low temperatures rubber becomes brittle, hydraulic fluids grow sticky, transmission cables slacken, pipe lines freeze, and metals lose some of their structural strength.

In spite of all these handicaps, high-altitude flying offers many operational advantages.  Weather conditions in the stratosphere are almost constant and do not even vary much with the latitude.  Due to the reduced drag of the rarefied air, it is possible to sustain the weight of the airplane at much higher speeds without additional thrust, if only the engine is kept going by "artificial respiration" through a supercharger.

# Chapter III

# The Planform of the Wing

### 20.  Vorticity

If air were a perfect, frictionless fluid without adhesion, the flow past a wing of long span would be described by the two-dimensional flow pattern of Fig. 3a.  The real pattern resulting from adhesion and viscosity is shown in Figs. 3b and 17.  In Fig. 3a, the rear stagnation point is located on the upper surface, and the air is compelled to flow with great velocity around the sharp trailing edge.  In Fig. 17, the flows above and below the wing join smoothly* at the trailing edge itself.  The streamline pattern of Fig. 3a does not yield lift and drag; the pattern of Fig. 17 does.

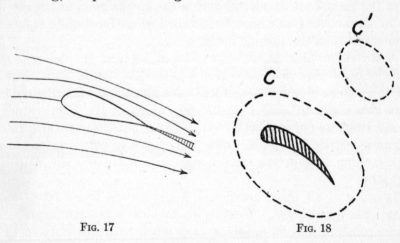

FIG. 17                          FIG. 18

Another significant difference between the flows shown in Figs. 3a and 3b may be described as follows.  Let a great number of observers be distributed in the two dimensional flow so as to form a chain $c$ which encloses, or a chain $c'$ which does not enclose, the wing profile (Fig. 18).  Every observer is to measure the velocity *component* $v_l$ of the air in the direction of his neighbor.  Multiplying the $v_l$ by the

* Fig. 17 shows the flow breaking loose on the upper surface near the trailing edge due to viscosity.

46

small distance $dl$ between observers, and adding, one obtains in the limit of vanishing $dl$ the line integral

$$\lim \Sigma v_l dl = \int v_l dl = \Gamma$$

along the closed chain $c$ or $c'$. The value $\Gamma$ of this integral is called *circulation value* or *vorticity* along the closed chain; $\Gamma$ is different in the two cases of Figs. 3a and 3b.

In the streamline pattern of Fig. 3a the vorticity has the value

$\Gamma = 0$ for *every* closed chain, $c$, enclosing the wing profile; and
$\Gamma = 0$ for *every* closed chain, $c'$, not enclosing the wing profile.

Thus Fig. 3a represents a circulationless or "irrotational flow," sometimes also called potential flow.

In the case of the actual flow of Fig. 3b or 17, one finds that

$\Gamma$ has one and the same fixed value for *every* chain $c$, and that
$\Gamma = 0$ for every chain $c'$.

We then say that Fig. 3b represents flow which has no circulation outside the wing, but has vorticity of value $\Gamma$ about the wing itself. $\Gamma$ is measured in ft²/sec.

Although the flow of Fig. 3b has the circulation value $\Gamma$ about the wing, this does not mean that the individual air particles move on closed paths encircling the wing.

A pattern in which the air particles really circulate about the wing is shown in Fig. 19, representing *pure circulation*. In this case again,

$\Gamma$ has one and the same fixed value for every chain $c$, and
$\Gamma = 0$ for every chain $c'$.

At large distances, $r$, from the body, the circulating streamlines of the pure circulation (Fig. 19) degenerate into circles on which the air velocity is

$$w = \Gamma/2\pi r$$

since
$$\Gamma = w \int dl = w 2\pi r \text{ for large } r.$$

Fig. 3b is obtained by superposition (vector addition) of the velocities found in the irrotational flow of Fig. 3a to the velocities in the pure circulation of Fig. 19. *Vice versa, flow of vorticity $\Gamma$ may always be represented as a superposition of irrotational flow and pure circulation.*

## 21. Kutta and Joukowsky's Theorem

So far we have described and defined what is meant by vorticity $\Gamma$ about a body, namely, $\Gamma = \int v_l dl$. Let us ask now, what is the *dynamic effect* of the vorticity, $\Gamma$, about a body of long span in two-dimensional flow?   The answer is given by the theorem of *Kutta* and *Joukowsky*:

*Circulation of value $\Gamma$ about a body of long span $b$ produces a force of lift, at right angles to the relative wind, of magnitude*

$$L = \rho V \Gamma b.$$

The proof of this law is given below.*

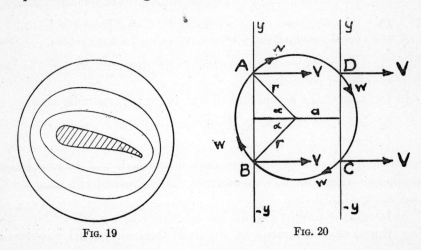

Fig. 19          Fig. 20

* When pure circulation is superimposed on wind, the resulting air velocity far from the body is the resultant of $V$ and of the circular velocity $w = \Gamma/2\pi r$.   This leads to a downward deflection of the incident airstream and an upward force in the following manner.   In the two-dimensional flow surrounding a body placed at the zero point of the $xy$-plane consider two vertical lines $y$-$y$ at large distance from the zero point, one in front, one abaft of the body.   These lines, as well as the body, may be considered to have "span" $b$ perpendicular to the $xy$-plane.   A small line element, $dy$, then represents an area $b \cdot dy$ perpendicular to the wind direction $x$.

Let us find the $y$-component of the *momentum* entering the area $b \cdot dy$ at two points $A$ and $B$ at equal distances above and below the body at elevations $+a$ and $-a$ (Fig. 20). The $x$-components of the velocity at $A$ and $B$ are $(V + w \cos \alpha)$ and $(V - w \cos \alpha)$ respectively, that is, $V$ in the *average* of $A$ and $B$.   The volume of air entering $b \cdot dy$ thus is $(b \cdot dy \cdot V)$ per second on the average.   Every cubic foot of air entering at $A$ or $B$ contains $y$-momentum of magnitude $\rho w_y$, that is,

$$\rho w_y = \rho w \cos \alpha = \rho(\Gamma/2\pi r)(a/r) = (\rho\Gamma/2\pi)(a/r^2) = (\rho\Gamma/2\pi)(a/a^2 + y^2)$$

Multiplying this by $(b \cdot dy \cdot V)$ one obtains the $y$-momentum entering the strip $(b \cdot dy)$ every second on the average.   Integrating over $y$ from $-\infty$ to $+\infty$ one obtains the total $y$-momentum entering the $y$-$y$ line from the left:

$$(b\rho V\Gamma/2\pi) \cdot \int_{-\infty}^{+\infty} dy \, a/(a^2 + y^2).$$

The value of the integral is $\pi$.   Therefore the upward $y$-component of momentum entering on the left is $\frac{1}{2}b\rho V\Gamma$ per second.   An equal amount of downward momentum leaves the $y$-$y$ line (of span $b$) on the right.   The total upward momentum imparted thereby to the body responsible for the deflection of the air thus becomes $b\rho V\Gamma$ per second.   According to Newton's law of motion, this equals the *upward force* on the body.   The result: Lift $= b\rho V\Gamma$, which is Kutta-Joukowsky's law.

Lift originates from the downward momentum imparted to the incoming horizontal air current. Because of the small density, the volume of air deflected downward every second must be comparatively large in order to produce a sizable lift force. The downward deflection is the result of wind $V$ and pure circulation $w$, as shown in the proof of K-J's law.

When a sphere, cylinder, or similar symmetrical body is put into an airstream, the air moves with equal velocity past the upper and the lower surfaces, and neither friction nor adhesion produces any clockwise or counter-clockwise circulation. Unsymmetrical bodies like airfoils, however, automatically surround themselves with a circulating airflow as soon as they are exposed to a steady airstream. This vorticity is produced and maintained in the following way.

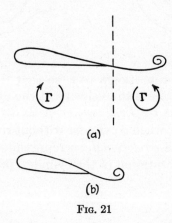

(a)

(b)

Fig. 21

The airflow at the first moment is "irrotational," as shown in Fig. 3a. The conflict between the large *upward* velocity near the sharp rear edge and adhesion to the edge itself gives rise to large shearing forces which produce a counter-clockwise whirl of vorticity $\Gamma$ called the *starting vortex* (Fig. 21a) and shown on plate C, page 22. According to the law of action and reaction, the starting vortex is always accompanied by a vorticity of opposite direction and of the same magnitude, $\Gamma$, which appears as circulation about the wing itself. Fig. 21 shows how the starting vortex is left behind or "washed away" by the wind, so that after some time the wing is surrounded only by the clockwise circulation of value $\Gamma$.

The process of developing the two vorticities during the start must be compensated by extra work against an extra "dynamic force" felt as *starting resistance*.

## 22.  The Rotor Ship

Circulation of air about a cylinder of radius $R$ may be enforced by artificial rotation of the cylinder itself.  The smokestack of a *rotor ship* viewed from above may rotate clockwise (Fig. 22).  The air particles on the surface do the same because of adhesion.  Those farther away are forced into circular paths by viscosity.  The result is a state of *pure circulation* in which the velocity $v$ at distance $r$ from

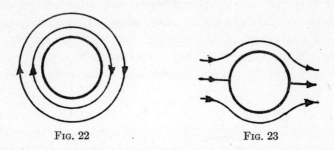

FIG. 22                          FIG. 23

the axis is inversely proportional to $r$, so that the product $v \cdot r$ equals the product $\bar{v} \cdot R$, where $\bar{v}$ is the velocity of the cylinder surface.  The vorticity of this flow is $\Gamma = \int v_l dl = v \cdot 2\pi r = \bar{v} \cdot 2\pi R$.

On the other hand, when a cylinder without rotation is exposed to a west wind, the flow is *irrotational*, as represented by Fig. 23.  West wind $V$, together with rotation of the cylinder, produces the pattern of

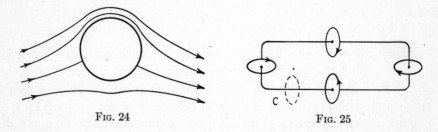

FIG. 24                          FIG. 25

Fig. 24, which is obtained by superposition of the velocities found in the patterns of Figs. 22 and 23.  The narrow streamtubes north of the cylinder signify suction, and the enlarged cross-section to the south indicates excess air pressure.  The resulting "lift" northward is

$$L = \rho V \Gamma b = \rho V \cdot \bar{v} 2\pi R \cdot b.$$

The same force may also be written

$$L = \rho V \bar{v} \pi S, \text{ where } S = 2Rb$$

$S$ is the cross-sectional area offered to the wind by the smokestack of diameter $2R$ and altitude $b$.

Let us compare this force with the air force on a *sail* or flat plate of area $S$ (section 11).

$$F = 0.64\rho V^2 S.$$

The ratio of the two forces is

$$\frac{L}{F} = \frac{\pi}{0.64} \cdot \frac{\bar{v}}{V} = 4.9\frac{\bar{v}}{V}.$$

That is, the air force on the rotating cylinder is as large as that on the sail if the rotating velocity is only $\frac{1}{5}$ of the wind velocity.

## 23.  Vortex Lines

In the last two sections we found that vorticity superimposed on wind produces *lift* at right angles to the incident wind in two-dimensional flow, without giving rise to a force of drag parallel to the wind. To explain and compute the drag on a wing in flight we must discuss the three-dimensional flow pattern near the wing tips and the peculiar vortices emerging from the tips and trailing behind the wing (*Prandtl's wing theory*).

In the case of two-dimensional flow we had to do with circulation about an infinite straight axis directed parallel to the infinite span. Let us consider now a finite, closed vortex line, and its most familiar example, the smoke ring.   Vortex lines are characterized by the fact that the circulation value $\Gamma = \int v_t dl$, measured along *any* closed chain $c$ (dotted line in Fig. 25) surrounding the vortex line, has *always*[*] the same constant value $\Gamma$, even if the vortex line itself becomes distorted in the course of time.   Therefore, one may speak of a vortex line of vorticity $\Gamma$ without referring to any particular enclosing chain, $c$, along which the vorticity is measured.

The fact that a vortex line cannot end anywhere in the fluid is related to this constant vorticity.   A vortex line either is closed within the fluid itself like a smoke ring, or it terminates on a solid body like a cyclone whose lower part ends on the ground and whose upper part runs to "infinity."   If a vortex line should end somewhere in the fluid (which it never does) the chain could be slipped over the end and then contracted to a point with a resulting circulation value of zero.

Another example of a vortex line is shown in Fig. 26.   Here a solid body is built around the part $AB$ of the line so that the "free

[*] As long as friction is negligible.   After a long time the vorticity dies down to smaller and smaller values, due to viscosity of the fluid.

part" of the vortex line begins at $B$, runs through $C$ and $D$ and ends on the solid body at $A$. The part $AB$ inside the body is called the "bound part" of the vortex line $ABCDA$. The air not only circulates about the free parts but about the bound part as well, so that *any* closed chain $c$ inside the fluid which cannot be stripped off the vortex line yields the same circulation value $\Gamma$, no matter whether the chain is drawn around the free or the bound part of the vortex line.

Fig. 26 gives a top view of the actual situation near and behind a wing, $AB$, surrounded by air circulation, when the wing moves to the left or when the wind blows to the right. The air circulation tak-

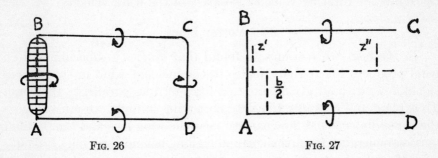

Fig. 26          Fig. 27

ing place about the *bound* part, $AB$, was discussed with Kutta-Joukowsky's law. $CD$ is the *starting vortex* left at the place of the take-off, or washed away with velocity $V$ in tunnel experiments. Bound and starting vortices are connected by the lines $BC$ and $AD$, which represent the *wing-tip vortices*. Their length increases steadily with velocity $V$ when the distance between starting vortex and wing increases. The increasing length means a steady addition of kinetic energy of circulation to the surrounding air. It is the source of a dynamic resistance called *induced drag*. Drag due to continuous ejection of vorticity from the wing tips constitutes the major part of wing resistance, augmented only by a small "skin friction drag."

## 24. Induced Drag and Downwash

The quantitative calculation of the induced drag due to wing-tip vorticity may be reduced to the problem of finding the direction and magnitude of the *mean wind* in which the wing finds itself as the result of the horizontal *incident wind*, V, and of the *downwash velocity* due to the wing-tip vorticity. (As seen in Fig. 26, the air flows downward through the whole area subtended by the vortex line $ABCDA$.) *Downwash velocity* designates only that part of the circulation which is due to the wing-tip vortices, without any contribution caused by the circulation about the wing axis $AB$ itself. The latter produces lift; our present aim is to find the drag.

Fig. 27 shows the plane $ABCDA$ and two points at distances $z'$ and $z''$ from the dotted central line; $z'$ is supposed to be located immediately behind the wing, whereas $z''$ lies far behind it. At $z''$ the wing-tip vortices $BC$ and $AD$ appear as vortex lines extending to *infinity* in both directions, whereas at the point $z'$ they appear as one-way infinite vortex lines. The circulating velocity at a point at distance $r$ from an infinite vortex line of circulation value $\Gamma$ is $w = \Gamma/2r\pi$. The downwash velocity at point $z''$ produced by the *two* vortices $BC$ and $AD$ thus is

$$w_\infty = \frac{\Gamma}{2\pi}\left(\frac{1}{(b/2)+z''}+\frac{1}{(b/2)-z''}\right).$$

This is the downwash velocity *far* (infinitely far) behind the wing. At the point $z'$ directly behind the wing, the downwash velocity produced by the two half-vortices is only half as large:

$$w_0 = \tfrac{1}{2}w_\infty = \frac{\Gamma}{4\pi}\left\{\frac{1}{(b/2)+z'}+\frac{1}{(b/2)-z'}\right\}.$$

Thus a wing section at distance $z'$ from the wing center is not only in the horizontal wind $V$, but also in the downwash $w_0$. The two together yield a *mean wind*, $V_0$, of slightly downward direction which gives rise to a Kutta-Joukowsky force, $F_0$, leaning slightly back from the vertical (see Fig. 32), with a horizontal component representing *drag*. This explanation of the induced drag is based on the assumption that vorticity emerges from the wing tips only, as pictured in Fig. 26.

## 25. Vortex Sheet

It may be considered that the vortex line $ABCDA$, of circulation value $\Gamma$, "enters" the wing at A and "leaves" it at B. Such a picture of a single vortex line through the wing is over-simplified, however. In reality, vortex lines enter the wing everywhere between A and O, and leave everywhere between O and B (Fig. 28). Instead of two linear wing-tip vortex lines trailing behind the wing, there is a whole vortex sheet consisting of many narrow ribbons of width $dz$ carrying various amounts of vorticity $d\Gamma$. [Fig. 28 is analogous to an electric current in a thin metal sheet headed by a thick metal wire $AB$, with current intensity $d\Gamma$ in the various sheet ribbons of width $dz$. The current elements $d\Gamma$ enter the wire all along $AO$ and leave all along $OB$, so that the current intensity $\Gamma$ in the wire itself increases from $A$ to $O$ and decreases from $O$ to $B$]. Since vorticity enters the wing $AB$ in small bits, $d\Gamma$, the value of $\Gamma$ along the wing increases gradually from the wing-tip $A$ to the center $O$ and decreases from $O$ to $B$ after reaching a maximum at $O$.

In our former simplified picture, the vorticity $\Gamma$ was *constant* all along the wing span. Actually, $\Gamma$ is a function, $\Gamma(z)$, of the coordinate $z$ along the span, with $\Gamma$ a maximum at $z = 0$. The distribution of vorticity along the span depends on the *planform* of the wing. Since $\Gamma$ determines the *lift* per unit length of span, the lift distribution $L(z)$ along the span also depends on the planform.

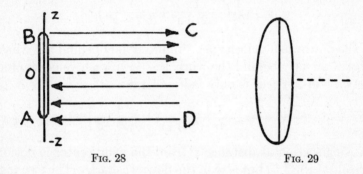

FIG. 28                    FIG. 29

Of particular interest is the elliptic $\Gamma$-distribution described by the formula

$$\Gamma(z) = \Gamma_{max}\sqrt{1 - (2z/b)^2}$$

and plotted in Fig. 29. This distribution of $\Gamma$ over the span length is realized when the planform consists of two semi-ellipses (Fig. 30). The *average* value of $\Gamma$ in this case is only slightly less than the maximum value, namely,

$$\Gamma_{average} = (\pi/4)\Gamma_{max} = 0.785\Gamma_{max}.$$

Fig. 29 shows $\Gamma$ increasing rapidly near the wing tips, but staying almost constant over most of the central part of the wing. This means that the influx and efflux of vorticity take place mainly near the wing-tips $A$ and $B$ (Fig. 28), which after all is not so very different from the former simplified picture of vorticity entering and leaving at the wing tips themselves (Fig. 26).

At a certain wing section at distance $z$ from the wing center, the lift per unit length of span is proportional to the circulation value: $L(z)$

$= \rho V b \Gamma(z)$, according to K-J.  Elliptic $\Gamma$-distribution thus leads to *elliptic lift distribution* (Fig. 31):

$$L(z) = L_{\max}\sqrt{1 - (2z/b)^2}, \; L_{\mathrm{av}} = (\pi/4) L_{\max}.$$

According to this formula, the lift is distributed almost evenly over the whole span $b$, and only the wing tips are relieved of load, which is of great advantage for structural reasons.

Elliptic $\Gamma$- and $L$-distribution has the outstanding feature of yielding a *constant downwash velocity, $w_0$, along the whole span* of value

$$w_0 = \Gamma_{\max}/2b = \Gamma_{\mathrm{av}} \cdot (2/b\pi), \text{ since } \Gamma_{\mathrm{av}} = (\pi/4)\pi\Gamma_{\max},$$

immediately behind the wing, and downwash $w_\infty = 2w_0$ far behind the wing.  Entering K-J's value $\Gamma = L/\rho V b$ for $\Gamma_{\mathrm{av}}$ in the last formula, one obtains

$$w_0 = 2L/\pi\rho V b^2, \text{ or } L = w_0\pi\tfrac{1}{2}\rho V b^2.$$

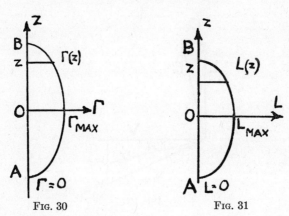

FIG. 30          FIG. 31

This may be written in the form

$$L = (b^2\pi w_0/VS) \cdot (\tfrac{1}{2}\rho V^2 S) = C_L(\tfrac{1}{2}\rho V^2 b)$$

and shows that the lift coefficient in the case of elliptic lift distribution is

$$C_L = \frac{b^2}{S} \cdot \frac{w_0}{V}\pi, \text{ where } \frac{b^2}{S} = \text{aspect ratio}.$$

## 26.  Lift/Drag Ratio

The continuous production of downward momentum of the air in the wake of the wing has two effects.  First, it produces *lift*.  Let us designate by "vol" the air volume which is "caught" by the wing per second and given a downward velocity $w_\infty$, observable far behind the wing.  The downward momentum imparted per second to the air then is the product $(\rho w_\infty \text{vol})$. According to Newton's law of motion, it must equal the upward force of reaction on the wing. We thus obtain the result

$$L = \rho w_\infty \text{vol.}$$

On the other hand, the same volume receives kinetic energy $\frac{1}{2}\rho w_\infty^2 \text{vol}$, at right angles to the direction $V$ of flight. The latter equals the work done per second by the propeller to overcome the induced *drag*. This work is the product of $D_iV$, so that we have

$$D_i = \frac{1}{2}\rho w_\infty^2 \text{vol}/V.$$

Combining the last two equations and remembering that $w_\infty = 2w_0$, we obtain the important relation

$$C_L/C_{D_i} = L/D_i = 2V/w_\infty = V/w_0.$$

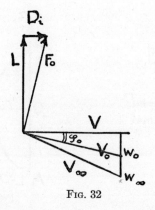

FIG. 32

The result is illustrated in Fig. 32. $V$ is the undisturbed horizontal wind velocity; $w_0$ and $w_\infty$ are the downwash velocities; $V$ and $w_0$ have as their resultant the "mean velocity," $V_0$, directly behind the wing (or at the place of the wing). $V$ and $w_\infty$ together yield the resultant velocity $V_\infty$ far behind the wing. Because of the small ratio $w/V$, the *downwash angle* $\varphi_0$ at the wing is approximately half the downwash angle $\varphi_\infty$ far behind. The mean wind, $V_0$, in which the wing finds itself, together with the air circulation $\Gamma$ about the wing, produces the resulting force, $F_0$, at right angles to $V_0$ and of value $F_0 = \Gamma\rho V_0 b$, with two components $L$ and $D_i$. Writing the last formula in product form, $D_iV = Lw_0$ and substituting for $w_0$ the value obtained in section 25, one obtains the work per second:

$$\text{Rate of work } D_iV = Lw_0 = 2L^2/\pi\rho V b^2$$

in ft-lbs when $\rho$ is measured in slugs, $L$ in lbs, and $V$ in ft/sec. In order to obtain the rate of work in horsepower, one has to divide by 550.

### Problems

(1) A wing of span 40 ft supports an airplane weighing 2000 lbs. Find the downwash velocity when the plane travels 100 miles/hr.

(2) At a certain angle of attack the downwash velocity, $w_0$, is 5 per cent of the speed $V$. The A.R. is 6. How large are the coefficients of lift and induced drag?

(3) An airfoil of span 35 ft must support 2000 lbs. Calculate the horsepower needed for overcoming the induced drag at a speed of 110 miles/hr. The same for a span of 40 ft.

### 27. Aspect Ratio

Large lift $L$ and large $L/D$ ratio at the same time are granted if the *product* $L \cdot L/D_i$ is large. Since

$$L = \rho V \Gamma_{av} b, \qquad L/D_i = V/w_0, \qquad w_0 = \Gamma_{av} 2/b\pi$$

we have

$$L \cdot L/D_i = \tfrac{1}{2}\rho V^2 \pi b^2 = \tfrac{1}{2}\rho V^2 S \pi (b^2/S).$$

That is, in order to secure maximum value of the product $L^2/D$ for given speed, V and given wing area, $S$, *the aspect ratio $b^2/S$ ought to be taken as large as possible*. For structural reasons it is seldom increased to more than 8/1.

*A large aspect ratio is most desirable for slow, heavy cargo planes.* Indeed, large weight, $W$, calls for equally large lift, $L = W$. The left of the last equation therefore is large. The small speed, $V$, would render the right-hand side small unless the factor $b^2/S$ is made large.

*Fast, light pursuit planes may have any conveniently small A.R.* Indeed, when $V^2$ on the right is large, $b^2/S$ does not have to be large, because $L = W$ on the left is not large.

The last equation may also be written in the inverted form

$$D_i = 2L^2/\rho V^2 \pi b^2.$$

That is, for given speed $V$ and given weight $W = L$, *the induced drag decreases as the square of the span increases.*

The same equation for $L^2/D_i$ in terms of the coefficient reads

$$C_L^2 = C_{D_i} \pi (b^2/S).$$

The two coefficients $C_L$ and $C_D$ vary slightly with the Reynolds number, $R = cV/\nu$. The lift coefficient, $C_L$, is approximately proportional to the angle of attack, $\alpha$, as long as $\alpha$ is small. In view of the downwash, $w_0$, at the wing, the effective angle of attack is not the angle $\alpha$ between chord $c$ and wind velocity $V$, but rather the angle $\alpha_0$ between $c$ and mean velocity $V_0$ (Fig. 33). Thus $\alpha = \alpha_0 + \varphi_0$, or, since $\varphi_0$ is small:

$$\alpha_0 = \alpha - \varphi_0 = \alpha - \text{tg } \varphi_0$$
$$= \alpha - D_i/L = \alpha - C_{D_i}/C_L$$
$$= \alpha - C_L S/b^2\pi.$$

The formulas of this section are helpful for calculating downwash and *induced* drag for various aspect ratios, $b^2/S$, from the lift curve $C_L$.

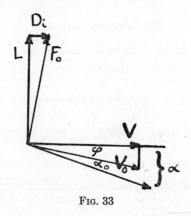

Fig. 33

Shearing forces in the boundary layer produce *skin friction drag* in addition to a small *eddy resistance*, which must not be confused with induced drag, although the latter is also due to vorticity behind the wing. Skin friction drag and eddy resistance together are known as *profile drag*, the value of which is practically independent of the angle of attack. It is not hard therefore to separate the "induced" from the "profile" drag if the total drag has been measured.

The streamline pattern breaks down completely at a certain large angle of attack known as the *burble point*, signifying the appearance of strong whirls behind the whole wing which increase the drag and reduce the lift to a considerable extent.

## 28. Parasite Resistance

The resistance of all parts of the airplane except the wings is designated as *parasite resistance* or *parasite drag*. Its value may be reduced by streamlining and fairing. External wires and bracings are to be streamlined with cross-sections similar to an airfoil profile. It is the purpose of the *radiator*, however, to offer as much surface as possible to the incoming airstream, thereby increasing the drag. The radiator surface may be reduced considerably by using an efficient cooling substance other than water (*e.g.*, Prestone). The surface and the drag are comparatively large in air-cooled engines. They may be reduced by partial covering or "cowling" of the cooling system.

The parasite drag of an airplane is expressed by the formula

$$D_{\text{par}} = C_{\text{par}}(\tfrac{1}{2}\rho V^2)S.$$

Since the coefficient $C_{\text{par}}$ depends on the Reynolds number, it may be determined in a wind tunnel. The surface, $S$, in the above formula stands for any significant area, *e.g.*, the cross-section of the fuselage. It is customary, however, to write $D_{\text{par}}$ in the same way as the drag on a flat plate (section 11), namely,

$$D_{\text{par}} = 1.28(\tfrac{1}{2}\rho V^2)S$$

where $S$ now is the *equivalent flat plate area*. That is, if the parasite resistance is as large as that of a flat plate of area 20 ft², we should substitute $S = 20$ ft² in the above formula, regardless of whether the actual surface responsible for the parasite drag is much larger than 20 ft².

The total drag of an airplane, *i.e.*, the sum of wing resistance and parasite drag, is

$$D = C_D(\tfrac{1}{2}\rho V^2)S_{\text{wing}} + 1.28(\tfrac{1}{2}\rho V^2)S_{\text{plate}}.$$

The total drag coefficient, as a factor of $\tfrac{1}{2}\rho V^2 S_{\text{wing}}$ therefore is

$$(C_D)_{\text{total}} = (C_D)_{\text{wing}} + 1.28(S_{\text{plate}}/S_{\text{wing}}).$$

The ratio $(S_{\text{plate}}/S_{\text{wing}})$ is called the "fineness" of the airplane. Account may be taken of the fact that the wind velocity at the rear of the airplane is somewhat larger than the incident wind $V$, because of the slipstream of the propeller.

# Chapter IV

# Biplanes

### 29. Lift and Drag of a Biplane

The main reason for using more than one wing is the desire to divide the large wing area into several parts of lighter and less expensive structure. The total wing area must be large enough to sustain the airplane at low landing speeds. According to the lift formula, the wing area is determined by the equation

$$S = L/(C_L \tfrac{1}{2} \rho V^2).$$

With a maximum value of $C_L = 1.6$ (see Fig. 15) and a landing speed of 60 miles/hr = 88 ft/sec, an airplane of weight $W = L = 24$ tons = 48,000 lbs would require a wing area of

$$S = 48,000/(1.6 \times \tfrac{1}{2} \times 0.002378 \times 88^2) = 3240 \text{ ft}^2.$$

For an aspect ratio of 5, this means a wing chord of 25.5 feet and a span of 127.5 feet. Such a large wing requires a strong internal structure which adds considerably to the weight, and a division of the wing area is very desirable. Through modern improvements in structural design and the introduction of aluminum-magnesium alloys, we are able today to built light and yet strong wings of large area, so that the monoplane dominates the field again. Its higher cost is counterbalanced by better maneuverability and a simplification of the problem of armament, fire power, etc. Tri- and multiplanes have only historic interest at the present time.

The two wings of a biplane may have different spans, $b_1$ and $b_2$. They may be either *staggered* or unstaggered, and they may be separated by a *gap*, which equals the perpendicular distance $a$. Stagger and gap are usually expressed in percentages as "stagger/chord ratio" and "gap/chord ratio."

The total *lift* of the two wings is a sum, $L_1 + L_2$. However, $L_1$ and $L_2$ are not identical with the original lifts of each single wing, because the excess pressure on the underside of the upper wing partly neutralizes the suction on the upper side of the lower wing, and *vice versa*. This effect may be reduced by increasing stagger and gap.

The total *drag* of the two wings consists first of the sum of the two *self-induced drags*, $D_1$ and $D_2$, arising from the dynamic resistance due to vortex sheet ejection by either wing. Secondly, there is an additional drag due to *mutual induction* of the first wing on the second, $D_{12}$, and of the second on the first, $D_{21}$. They are due to the fact that the circulation surrounding vortex sheet 1 reaches into the range of sheet 2 and increases the circulation velocity about sheet 2, and *vice versa*. This mutual interference leads to the total induced drag:

$$D_i = D_1 + D_2 + (D_{12} + D_{21}).$$

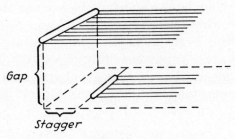

Gap

Stagger

Fig. 34

The *mutually induced drag*, $D_{12} + D_{21}$, *is independent of stagger*, since superposition of the two circulations takes place only where the two vortex sheets are one above the other, independent of the length of any "free parts."

According to section 27, the self-induced drags are proportional to the square of the lifts $L_1$ and $L_2$, respectively:

$$D_1 = (2/\pi\rho V^2)\cdot(L_1/b_1)^2, \qquad D_2 = (2/\pi\rho V^2)\cdot(L_2/b_2)^2.$$

The mutually induced drag is proportional to the product $L_1L_2$ and inversely proportional to the product $b_1b_2$; it may be written in the form

$$(D_{12} + D_{21}) = (2/\pi\rho V^2)(L_1L_2/b_1b_2)2\sigma$$

where $\sigma$ is a numerical factor called *coefficient of mutual induction*. This coefficient does not depend on the size but only on the *relative* dimensions of the two-wing system, in particular on the span ratio $b_1/b_2$ and on the *ratio* between gap $a$ and average span $\frac{1}{2}(b_1 + b_2)$. The coefficient $\sigma$ is independent of the stagger. Adding the self-induced and mutually induced drags, one obtains the following expression for the total drag in terms of the lifts:

$$D_i = \frac{2}{\pi \rho V^2}\left\{\left(\frac{L_1}{b_1}\right)^2 + \left(\frac{L_2}{b_2}\right)^2 + 2\sigma\frac{L_1 L_2}{b_1 b_2}\right\}.$$

This result is helpful in discussing the merits of the biplane as compared with the monoplane.

## 30. Monoplane versus Biplane

The reason for constructing biplanes is the advantage of dividing the large wing area in two smaller parts. The question remains whether this advantage is not nullified by inferior flying characteristics, in particular by diminished lift and increased drag. In order to discuss this problem let us compare a monoplane of large wing area, $S$, with a biplane whose wings have area $S_1$ and $S_2$ respectively, and have the same *shape* as the monoplane wing, meaning the same wing profile and aspect ratio, so that the lift *coefficients* $C_L$ of all three wings, $S$, $S_1$, and $S_2$ are identical at every angle of attack.

When the monoplane and the biplane support the same load at the same speed, $V$, we have $L = W = L_1 + L_2$, or

$$C_L(\tfrac{1}{2}\rho V^2)S = W = C_L(\tfrac{1}{2}\rho V^2)S_1 + C_L(\tfrac{1}{2}\rho V^2)S_2,$$

from which we learn that

$$S = S_1 + S_2.$$

That is, the total wing area of the biplane wings must be equal to that of the monoplane wing. Because of their similar shapes, this means the relation $b^2 = b_1{}^2 + b_2{}^2$ between the spans.

The induced *drag* of the monoplane is

$$D_{\mathrm{mon}} = (2/\pi\rho V^2)(w/b)^2.$$

The induced drag of the biplane depends on the gap. Let us take the most favorable case of a very *large gap* where the mutual induction vanishes ($\sigma = 0$). Also let $S_1 = S_2$ and $b_1 = b_2$. In this case one also has $L_1 = L_2 = \tfrac{1}{2}L$ and $b_1{}^2 = b_2{}^2 = \tfrac{1}{2}b^2$. Therefore one obtains

$$D_{\mathrm{bipl}} = (2/\pi\rho V^2)[(L_1/b_1)^2 + (L_2/b_2)^2]$$
$$(2/\pi\rho V^2)(\tfrac{1}{2}W^2/\tfrac{1}{2}b^2) = (2/\pi\rho V^2)(W/b)^2.$$

That is, for a large gap the biplane drag is exactly as large as the monoplane drag, on the assumption that both planes have to carry the same weight at the same speed. Thus, if the gap is made large enough, the division of $S$ in two parts $S_1 + S_2$ does not diminish the $L/D$ ratio.

A slight increase of $D$ and decrease of $L$ for a smaller gap is acceptable as the price for allowing a lighter construction of the two smaller wings of the biplane. On the other hand, the flying characteristics may be improved by choosing a large aspect ratio. The reason for keeping the latter below 6 to 8 is constructional. With light metals of great strength one may build large wings of large A.R. without excessive weight of the internal structure; for this reason the monoplane has come into the foreground again.

**Problem.** How does the drag of a biplane with two equal wings and mutual induction coefficient $\sigma = 1/8$ compare with the drag of a monoplane having the same wing shape?

### 31.  Load Distribution in Biplanes

The distribution of the load between the two wings of a biplane depends on the stagger. Positive stagger, with upper wing ahead, puts more load on the upper wing. The opposite holds for negative stagger. The gap/chord ratio has little influence on the load ratio, except for small angles of attack.

When the two wings are set at different angles of attack, one speaks of *decalage*. The latter is positive when the angle between the wings opens in the direction of flight. Positive decalage boosts the load on the upper wing; negative decalage decreases it.

The wind force on a single airfoil attacks at the c.p. located on the chord. In the biplane, however, two wind forces (loads), $F_1$ and $F_2$, attack on the chords $c_1$ and $c_2$, respectively. The result is equivalent to a force, $F = F_1 + F_2$, attacking on a new intermediate center of pressure, which is located on an intermediate *mean chord* between $c_1$ and $c_2$. The distances $a_1$ and $a_2$ of the mean chord from the single chords are determined by the condition of equal moments of force: $F_1a_1 = F_2a_2$ where $a_1 + a_2 = a$ is the distance between the single chords. From these two equations one obtains the distances

$$a_1 = aF_1/(F_1+F_2), \qquad\qquad a_2 = aF_1/(F_1+F_2).$$

The mean chord and the mean c.p. play the same role for the stability of the biplane as do chord and c.p. for the monoplane. A certain "mean leading edge" on the mean chord serves as the pivot of the pitching moment. Lift, drag, and pitching moment are given by formulas similar to those of section 12, except that $S$ is the total area of the two wings. The characteristic curves for the coefficients $C_L$,

$C_D$, and $C_M$ of the double wing are not the same as those of the same wings separately.　They may be obtained, however, from the single-wing curves by numerical *correction factors* which depend on the gap/chord and stagger/chord ratios, but are practically independent of the angle of attack; they apply to the characteristic curve as a whole.

# Chapter V

## Stability and Control

### 32. Roll, Pitch, and Yaw

Equilibrium may be defined as the state of a body in which the total force, $F$, as well as the total torque or moment of force, $M$, vanishes. The equilibrium is *stable* when any variation from the equilibrium position produces counterforces and torques which tend to restore the body to its original *position*. (Example: an airplane model suspended at its center of gravity in a wind tunnel). An airplane traveling straight ahead at constant speed is in stable equilibrium when any disturbance sets up forces which restore it to its original state of *uniform motion*, rather than position, and to its original *orientation* in space with respect to three fixed directions, *XYZ*, in space.

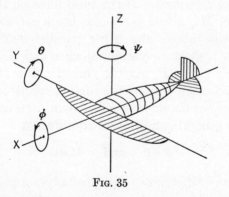

Fig. 35

The orientation, also called the *attitude*, of an airplane is described by the direction of three *body axes* fixed in the airplane itself, namely, a longitudinal $x$-axis parallel to the propeller shaft, a lateral $y$-axis parallel to the span, and a $z$-axis pointing upward (Fig. 35), with the center of gravity as zero point.

(a) The longitudinal $x$-axis points in the forward direction of flight. An upward turn of the positive $x$-axis through an angle $\Theta$ is called *pitch*. Nosing down results in a negative pitching angle $\Theta$. A turn

65

of the longitudinal $x$-axis to the right is called (positive) *yaw*, and is measured by the yawing angle $\psi$.

(b) The lateral or $y$-axis is directed parallel to the span. *Bank* or *roll* is measured by the banking angle $\phi$ of the $y$-axis with respect to the horizontal. The airplane is "banked to the right" when the right wing is lower than the left. Right bank is the attitude taken during a turn of the airplane to the right, and left bank belongs to a turn to the left. When the lateral $y$-axis turns to the right it yields positive yaw, as in (a).

(c) The positive $z$-axis points upward. A backward tilt of the $z$-axis yields positive pitch $\Theta$, as in (a). Tilting of the $z$-axis to the right results in right bank or roll, as in (b). Roll or bank through the angle $\phi$ is produced by a banking moment or torque, $M_z$, about the longitudinal $x$-axis. Pitch, $\Theta$, results from a rotation about the lateral $y$-axis and is produced by a pitching moment, $M_y$. Yaw is the result of a yawing torque, $M_z$, about the vertical $z$-axis.

The magnitude of a torque depends on the attacking force and on the axis of rotation determining the lever arm. The value of $M_x$ changes if the $x$-axis is shifted parallel to itself in the $y$- or $z$-direction. However, there is a simple rule controlling the change of torque during a parallel shift of the axis of reference: If the total force on the body *vanishes*, and if the torque, $M_x$, about *one* $x$-axis has a certain value, then $M_x$ has the same value about any other parallel $x$-axis. The same is true for $M_y$ with respect to various $y$-axes, and for $M_z$ and various $z$-axes. Since any point, $P$, may be considered as the intersection of an $x$-, $y$-, and $z$-axis, one obtains the further result*: *If the total force vanishes, the torque has the same value about any axis and any pivot point, $P$*. That is, the general condition of equilibrium

$$F = 0 \quad \text{and} \quad M = 0$$

does not require any reference to a particular pivot point or a particular axis for the torque, $M$.

It is very convenient, however, to refer the torque to the center of gravity as pivot point. The c.g. is defined as the point for which the torque of gravity vanishes. The equilibrium condition, $M = 0$

---

* The torque $M$, when regarded as a vector in the direction of the axis of rotation, is the sum of the vector products of the small forces $f$ and lever arms $l$. The torques about two different pivot points, $P$ and $P'$, are sums of vector products:

$$M = \Sigma f \times l \quad \text{and} \quad M' = \Sigma f \times l' = \Sigma f \times (l'-l) + \Sigma f \times l$$

where $l$ and $l'$ are the vectors from $P$ and $P'$ to the points of attack of the small forces, $f$. Hence $l'-l$ is the constant vector from $P'$ to $P$, so that $\Sigma f \times (l-l') = (l'-l) \times F$ vanishes when $F = 0$. Therefore, $M = M'$ when $F = 0$.

then requires only that the torque about the c.g. of the other forces, namely, wind force and propeller thrust, shall vanish, too.   Furthermore, if the propeller axis is laid through or almost through the c.g., it contributes only a negligible torque about the c.g.   Equilibrium is granted under these circumstances (a) when the total force vanishes, or (b) when the torque of the *wind force* about the c.g. vanishes:

$$\begin{cases} \text{weight} + \text{propeller thrust} + \text{wind force} = 0, \\ \text{wind torque} = 0 \text{ about c.g.} \end{cases}$$

Stability against change of orientation is granted, therefore, if any disturbance of the orientation leads to a restoring counter-torque of the *wind force* about the c.g., irrespective of the propeller thrust and the weight of the airplane.

## 33.   Static and Dynamic Stability

Stable equilibrium or balance of the airplane in a certain attitude (for instance, $\phi = \Theta = \psi = 0$) occurs when the following conditions are satisfied:

(1) The three components of the wind torque about the c.g. must vanish in the position of equilibrium: $M_x = M_y = M_z = 0$.

(2) When $\phi$ is increased (decreased), $M_x$ must become negative (positive), so that any disturbance of $\phi$ is counteracted by a *restoring moment*.   The same must apply to $\Theta$ and $M_y$, as well as to $\psi$ and $M_z$.

If a growing angle of bank were accompanied by an increase of the banking moment, this would lead to a further increase of $\phi$, and so forth.   The equilibrium would be *unstable*, and the slightest disturbance of the banking angle would result in an ever-growing bank.

But even under conditions (1) and (2) of stable "static" equilibrium, the airplane usually does not simply return to its equilibrium position but overshoots its mark in the opposite direction, then swings back, and carries out *oscillations* about the position of equilibrium.   If the amplitudes decrease to smaller and smaller values, the static equilibrium is *dynamically stable*, too.   If the oscillations go on with constant amplitude, one has a state of *neutral dynamic equilibrium* with continuous roll, pitch, and yaw.   If the oscillating amplitudes are growing, the airplane is said to be *dynamically unstable*, even though static equilibrium may exist according to conditions (1) and (2).

If the restoring moments are small, the airplane has a low degree of stability; in this case the pilot must be constantly on his guard to correct excessive deviations from equilibrium. Large restoring moments, on the other hand, make the plane *stiff*, and reduce its maneuverability. Pursuit planes are given a low degree of stability so that they may react quickly to the controls. A transport plane, on the other hand, when given a sufficient degree of stability, may be flown on a straight course with hands off the controls.

Static equilibrium is built into the airplane by a proper distribution of the weight and the wind force. Dynamic stability depends on external circumstances. Excessive speed may produce periodic pressure fluctuations, giving rise to undamped oscillations similar to the fluttering of a weather vane or to the up and down pitch of a fast motor boat.

The *period* of oscillation about an axis of rotation depends on the moment of inertia about the axis. The three moments of inertia about the x-, y-, and z-axes of an airplane have three different values. Therefore the periods of the respective oscillations do not agree. The combination of roll, pitch, and yaw with three different periods is extremely annoying for the pilot if the three amplitudes are not kept within small limits.

### 34.  Longitudinal Stability

The conditions of static equilibrium against pitch are:

(1)  $M_y = 0$

for $\Theta_{equ}$

(2)  $dM_y/d\Theta < 0$

where $d\Theta$ describes a small increment of $\Theta$, and $dM_y$ is the corresponding increment of $M_y$. The second condition requires a decrease of the pitching moment with increasing pitching angle, $\Theta$. That is, when $M_y$ is plotted against $\Theta$, the curve must have negative slope at $\Theta_{equ}$, where $M_y = 0$ (Fig. 36). The slope of the curve depends on the position of wing and tail relative to the c.g. The contributions of gravity and thrust to the torque about the c.g. are zero; thus $M_y$ is the torque of the wind force about the c.g.

**Influence of the wing.** As explained in section 14, cambered wings in contrast to flat plates, have unstable travel of the c.p., at least for small angles of attack, $\alpha$. The same is true for small pitching angles, $\Theta$, of the airplane. That is, when $\Theta$ is increased, the c.p. of the wing, and with it the line of action of the wind force on the wing, travels forward along the chord. If the wing is mounted forward of the c.g. this means that increasing $\Theta$ leads to a growing lever arm of the wind torque about the c.g., tending to increase $\Theta$ further; thus the wing is unstable against pitch. However, stability is restored by the tail.

**Influence of the tail.** The long lever arm from the c.g. to the horizontal tail surface yields a powerful stabilizing torque against pitch. Whenever the airplane noses up (with tail depressed) the

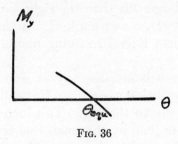

FIG. 36

horizontal tail surface receives additional *lift*, which tends to restore the original position. The restoring torque is particularly large if the characteristic curve for the lift coefficient of the tail-wing rises steeply with increasing angle $\alpha$.

### 35. Lateral Stability

Due to the fact that the pitching moment, $M_y$, depends on the pitching angle $\Theta$ only, and is independent of roll, $\phi$, and yaw, $\psi$, pitching is independent of other deviations from the equilibrium. The three lateral motions, roll, yaw, and side slip, however, are interrelated. Roll always involves yaw and side slip, and *vice versa*. The magnitude of the torques, $M_x$ and $M_z$, and of the force, $F_y$, depend on the three variables $\phi$, $\psi$, and $y$ (side slip) simultaneously. Equilibrium requires that the three partial differential quotients $\partial M_x/\partial \phi$, $\partial M_x/\partial \psi$, and $\partial M_x/\partial y$ be negative. The same is required for the differential quotients of $M_z$ and $F_y$. Altogether there are *nine* interrelated equilibrium conditions to be satisfied simultaneously in order to make lateral stable equilibrium possible. Only a few of these conditions will be discussed in the following.

Lateral stability against roll is secured by a positive *dihedral* angle, with the tips of the wings higher than the root. In order to understand the effect of dihedral let us first consider a wing without dihedral, with its leading edge raised to a certain angle of attack, $\alpha$, as exemplified by an open book whose upper edge is raised slightly from the table. If now the wing tips (corresponding to the right and left book edges) are lifted slightly so as to yield dihedral, the angles between the wing chords and the relative wind decrease to a value, $\alpha'$, less than $\alpha$. If the wings were folded completely together, $\alpha$ would shrink to zero (like a closed book held vertically between the hands). If the airplane with dihedral is banked to the left, the left wing will recover its former angle of attack, $\alpha$, whereas the right wing will have a still smaller angle, $\alpha''$. Since the lift force increases with the angle of attack, the left wing is subject to a larger lift than the right wing; the airplane thus will tend to restore itself to an even keel. A small dihedral angle of $2°$ to $4°$ yields sufficient lateral restoring moment without rendering the plane too "stiff."

Stability against roll is increased by an excess of *fin area* (above the c.g.) over *keel area* (below the c.g.). If the plane banks to the left it also begins to sideslip to the left. This increases the pressure on the large fin area more than on the small keel area, and the resulting torque counteracts the bank and restores the airplane to its normal attitude.

### 36. Directional Stability

Directional stability of an airplane is maintained by the vertical tail surface. During a deviation to the right, the tail rudder presents its left surface to the wind and produces a restoring moment, just as a weather vane always tends to point in the direction of the wind. Because of the long lever arm, the restoring moment of the tail rudder is comparatively large.

A smaller contribution to directional stability may be obtained from the wing itself if the tips are swept back from the wing root. The wing chord, in the case of *sweepback*, does not point in the direction of travel; as a result, the relative wind parallel to the chord, $V'$, is smaller than the speed, $V$, of the airplane. This reduction of the relative wind results in a corresponding reduction of the drag as compared to the drag in normal wing position. If, however, the airplane is yawed to the right, the left wing swings into the normal position with chord parallel to $V$, so that the drag is increased, whereas the right wing is subject to a still smaller drag due to its farther displacement from normal. The wind torque set up during the yaw thus tends to restore the original course.

### 37. The Control Surfaces

The control surfaces of an airplane are the rudder, the elevator, and the ailerons. A control surface in neutral position, together with the fixed surface to which it is hinged, represents an airfoil without camber (Fig. 37a). A turn of the movable part, however, transforms it into a *cambered airfoil* set at a certain angle of attack to the wind (Fig. 37b). The effect obtained in this way is much greater than if both the parts turned together into the same new angle of attack. The movable part must not be turned too far, however, since large angles of attack cause a considerable reduction of the lift and a large increase of the drag due to burbling.

The three control surfaces act as follows. When the *rudder* is pulled to the right, the tail is given an additional "lift" to the left which swings it to the left and yaws the airplane to the right, as desired. When the pilot pulls the *elevator* stick toward him, the elevator moves upward, and the horizontal tail has negative camber. This yields additional tail load, in response to which the airplane noses up. The *ailerons* are geared through transmissions so that one aileron flaps

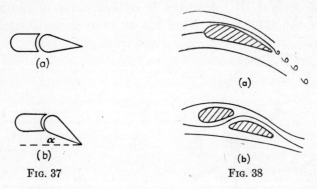

(a)

(b)

Fɪɢ. 37

(a)

(b)

Fɪɢ. 38

down and the other one up. The corresponding increase and decrease of the camber produces a lift increase and decrease on the right and left wing, respectively, which results in a banking moment. If the left wing is banked down due to a decrease of its lift, it also suffers a decrease of drag; thus the airplane is subject to a yawing moment to the right. This right yaw is offset by more left rudder (remember that the left bank was occasioned by a turning movement to the left). Banking without turning leads to sideslip; this is an example of the mutual interdependence of the various deviations and torques. *Sideslip* during a turn is defined as a motion toward the center of curvature, whereas *skidding* is a motion in the opposite direction.

A constant undesired yaw is produced by the air current of the rotating propeller. When the propeller rotates clockwise as viewed from the cockpit, the fin above the c.g. is subject to an additional wind pressure on the left, and the keel on the right, resulting in a *slip-stream twist*. For reasons of stability the fin area is larger than the keel area.   The slipstream thus tends to swing the airplane to the left when the propeller turns clockwise.   This effect may be offset by mounting the fin with a slight yaw, so that it serves as a permanent rudder.

Much effort has been spent on the task of landing safely at low speed.   A partial solution of this problem is obtained by wings fitted with *slots*.   Low landing speed requires an increase of the lift coefficient, obtained by an increase of the angle of attack.   If the wing is pitched up too far, however, the air on the upper wing surface begins to burble, and the plane stalls (Fig. 38a).   If the slot is opened (Fig. 38b) the air runs smoothly along the entire upper surface, and stalling is avoided in spite of the large angle of attack.

### 38.   Dynamic Load

When a weight, $W$, describes a *vertical circle* of radius $r$ with velocity $V$, the supporting string has to exert a centripetal force of

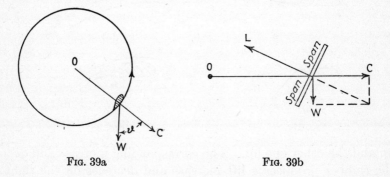

FIG. 39a                    FIG. 39b

magnitude $C = WV^2/r$ poundals $= WV^2/rg$ lbs (where $g = 32.2$).   The total tensile force exerted by the string (see Fig. 39a) is:

$$F = C + W \cos \vartheta = W(V^2/rg + \cos \vartheta)$$

where $\vartheta$ is the angle between string and vertical.   In particular, at the bottom and top of the circle the supporting force is

$$F = C + W \text{ or } C - W$$

respectively.   The same considerations apply to an airplane describing a *vertical loop* of radius $r$ with velocity $V$.   The tensile force of the string is to be replaced by an extra wind force toward the center of the loop of magnitude $C = WV^2/rg$ lbs counterbalancing the centrifugal force of the same amount.   In other words, the wing has to support an extra *dynamic load* of magnitude $C$, to which is added the *basic load*, $W$, so as to yield the *applied load*, $C + W$, at the bottom of the loop. The applied load at the top is $C - W$. In both cases the applied load is at right angles to the path, and is opposite the lift which is always perpendicular to the path. The lift to be applied at the bottom of the loop is $W + C$. It may be produced by an increased angle of attack, so that the lift coefficient, $C_L$, supporting the weight in level flight at speed $V$, is increased to a larger value, $C'_L$. This larger value is determined in the following way. Whereas in level flight one has $W = C_L(\frac{1}{2}\rho V^2)S$, the applied load at the bottom is

$$F = W + C = W[1 + (V^2/rg)] = C_L(\tfrac{1}{2}\rho V^2)S[1 + (V^2/rg)]$$

for which one may write

$$F = C'_L(\tfrac{1}{2}\rho V^2)S, \text{ where } C'_L = C_L[1 + (V^2/rg)].$$

That is, the angle of attack at the bottom of the loop has to be increased so much that the lift coefficient increases from $C_L$ to $C'_L$. If the wing is to withstand the applied load it must be made much stronger than if it had to support only the basic load. For reasons of safety the wing structure ought to withstand *twice* the maximum applied load to which the wing might ever be exposed. If the latter is 5 times the basic load, the factor of safety would have to be as large as $2 \times 5 = 10$.

A similar dynamic load appears when the airplane describes a *horizontal circle* of radius $r$. Fig. 39b shows an airplane travelling straight into the plane of the paper. The angle of bank is adjusted so that the resultant of gravity and centrifugal force is perpendicular to the wing span. The correct banking angle is determined by the equation

$$\tan \phi = C/W = V^2/rg.$$

Without banking the airplane would *skid* away from the center of curvature; if the angle $\phi$ is too large, the airplane would *sideslip* toward the center of curvature. The correct angle $\phi$ depends on the radius of curvature and the speed $V$, but is independent of the weight of the airplane. The applied load in the case of a horizontal circle is $\sqrt{C^2 + W^2}$ (see Fig. 39b). It must be counteracted by an increased lift whose direction is perpendicular to the banked span. If the airplane describes a *spiral* of comparatively small pitch, the angle $\phi$ and the applied load may still be obtained from the above formula.

A dynamic load of a different kind arises whenever the airplane is suddenly brought to a smaller or larger velocity. Let $V_0$ be the original horizontal speed and $C_L^0$ the lift coefficient for the angle $\alpha$, so that

$L_0 = W = C_L^0(\frac{1}{2}\rho V_0^2)S$. If the pilot wants to decelerate to the smaller speed $V_1$ he must pull the wing into a larger angle of attack, $\alpha_1$, so that the new lift coefficient $C_L^1$, together with the smaller velocity, satisfies the equation $W = C_L^1(\frac{1}{2}\rho V_1^2)S$. If he jerks his plane into the new angle $\alpha_1$, the speed at the first instant would still be $V_0$, so that the lift force is determined by the new coefficient $C_L^1$ and by the original speed $V_0$, namely,

$$L_1 = C_L^1(\frac{1}{2}\rho V_0^2)S \quad \text{whereas} \quad L_0 = W = C_L^0(\frac{1}{2}\rho V_0^2)S = C_L^1(\frac{1}{2}\rho V_1^2)S.$$

The load $L_1$, at the first instant of jerking the plane into the new angle $\alpha_1$ (which is adjusted to the new velocity $V_1$), thus is larger than the normal load. The ratio is, according to the above equations,

$$L_1/W = L_1/L_0 = V_0^2/V_1^2.$$

If the pilot wants to slow down to one-half the original speed and applies the elevator too suddenly, he will increase the load to four times the normal weight. At the same time the airplane will be given a sudden upward acceleration of value $[(V_0^2/V_1^2) - 1]g$. Indeed, the upward force is $L_1$ and the downward force of gravity is $L_0 = W$, so that the resultant force is $L_1 - L_0 = [(V_0^2/V_1^2) - 1]W$ resulting in the upward acceleration just mentioned.

### Problems

(1) An airplane weighing 8000 lbs, 200 ft² in wing area and travelling at 120 miles/hr is suddenly pulled into a new angle of attack 3° larger than the original one. Find the instantaneous load in the new position and the upward acceleration. Use characteristic curves (Fig. 15).

(2) An airplane weighing 7000 lbs, 150 ft² in wing area and travelling at 90 miles/hr runs into an upward air current of velocity 5 ft/sec. Find the new angle of attack and the upward acceleration. Use characteristic curves (Fig. 15).

(3) A plane weighing 7500 lbs describes a curve of radius 800 ft at a speed of 90 miles/hr. Find the banking angle and the new load.

(4) When soaring on a horizontal circle at 40 miles/hr the wing load shall not exceed the normal load by more than 3 times. Find the shortest radius of curvature permitted in this case, and the corresponding banking angle.

### 39. Equilibrium in Rectilinear Flight

The drag resulting from the force components parallel to the wind may be considered to attack at the *center of resistance*, which is defined as the point about which the *moment* of drag is zero. The weight attacks at the center of gravity (c.g.) along a vertical line of action. The tail wing, including the elevator, either contributes a small lift or a *tail load* perpendicular to the wind. Figs. 40, 41, and 42 show the various forces and lever arms in the cases of climb, dive, and horizontal

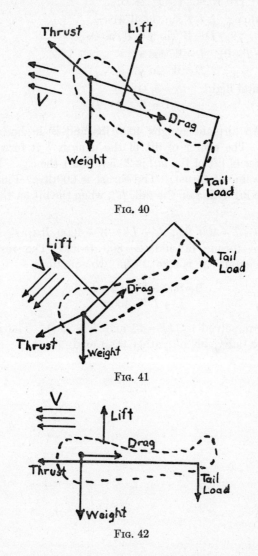

FIG. 40

FIG. 41

FIG. 42

flight. Since the thrust, $T$, parallel to the longitudinal axis through the c.g., and the weight, $W$, have lever arms of *zero*, they do not contribute to the pitching moment, $M_y$. Clockwise and counter-clockwise moments cancel in the case of equilibrium. The following relations between weight $W$, lift $L$, thrust $T$, drag $D$, angle $\Theta$ between thrust and direction of flight $V$, and angle $\gamma$ between horizontal and $V$ are helpful for the solution of practical problems.

(1) Climb: $L + T \sin \Theta = W \cos \gamma$,
$\qquad\qquad D + W \sin \gamma = T \cos \Theta$.

(2) Power dive: $L + T \sin \Theta = W \cos \gamma$,
$\qquad\qquad\quad D - W \sin \gamma = T \cos \Theta$.

(3) Glide: $(T = 0)$ $\quad L = W \cos \gamma$,
$\qquad\qquad\qquad\quad D = W \sin \gamma$.

(4) Horizontal flight: $(\gamma = 0, \Theta = 0)$
$\qquad\qquad\qquad\quad L = W, D = T$.

*Example:* An airplane weighs 4000 lbs and is in horizontal flight at constant speed. The center of lift of the *wing* is $\frac{1}{2}$ ft forward of the c.g., whereas the center of lift of the *tail* is 29.5 ft abaft the c.g. The line of drag is 2 ft under the line of thrust. The thrust is 600 lbs. Find direction and magnitude of the lift acting on the tail, $L''$, when the lift on the wing is called $L'$.

*Solution:* $D = T = 400$ lbs; $L' + L'' = W = 4000$ lbs; $T$ and $D$ yield a counter-clockwise torque of $400 \times 2 = 800$ ft-lbs. The resulting counter-clockwise torque about c.g. is zero. The two equations

$$0 = 800 + L'' 29.5 - L' 0.5,$$
$$L' + L'' = 4000$$

for $L'$ and $L''$ are solved by $L'' = 40$ and $L' = 3960$. The plus sign of $L''$ confirms that the tail yields lift rather than load.

# Chapter VI

# Performance

## 40. Airplane Characteristics

The performance of an airplane in flight is determined by the following factors:

(1) The characteristic curves for the lift and drag coefficients, $C_L$ and $C_D$; the coefficient $C_M$ of the moment about the center of pressure of the wing; and the curve describing the position of the c.p. at various angles of attack in per cent of the chord.
(2) The "equivalent flat plate area" of the other parts of the airplane for determination of the parasite drag.
(3) The weight.
(4) Certain engine-propeller characteristics, namely,
  (a) the maximum horsepower at the rated rpm delivered at maximum speed;
  (b) the horsepower delivered at various lower speeds with smaller rpm;
  (c) the reduction factor of efficiency of the propeller, that is, the ratio of power available to power delivered at various speeds.

Information is desired on the following traditional items of performance:

(1) the horsepower required at various speeds and altitudes;
(2) the rate of climb at various altitudes;
(3) the maximum altitude and the service ceiling;
(4) the best gliding angle;
(5) the range.

With the help of the material collected in the foregoing chapters we now are in a position to discuss these items individually.

## 41. Horsepower Required

The horsepower required to fly an airplane at different horizontal speeds at various altitudes may be derived from the characteristic curves of the wing, or in the case of biplanes, from the corrected curves for the two-wing system (section 31). Since $L = W$ in level flight, and the power is the product of drag and velocity, we arrived in section 17 at the following formulas for the speed and the horsepower required for the wing:

$$V = \sqrt{W/\tfrac{1}{2}\rho S C_L}, \quad \text{horsepower} = \sqrt{W^3/\tfrac{1}{2}\rho S}(C_D/C_L^{2/3})/550,$$

with $\rho$ in slugs per ft³ and $W$ in lbs. The first formula shows that the speed depends on the *wing loading*, $W/S$, or the weight per square foot of the wing surface. Since $C_L$ and $C_D$ are functions of the angle of attack, the two formulas allow us to plot $V$ as well as the horsepower required against $\alpha$ in two separate curves which are valid for a certain density, preferably for standard sea level $\rho_0 = 0.002378$ slug/ft³. The additional horsepower required for overcoming the parasite drag is (section 28):

$$\text{parasite hp} = \text{wing hp} \times 1.28 \ (S_{\text{plate}}/S_{\text{wing}})$$

where $S_{\text{plate}}$ is the equivalent flat plate area of the other parts of the airplane. [Special account may be taken of the fact that the propeller

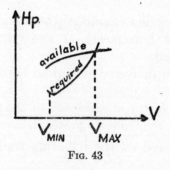

FIG. 43

sends a slipstream of velocity larger than $V$ over the rear parts of the airplane and thereby increases the parasite drag]. The two separate curves may be used for plotting a single *curve* (Fig. 43) which shows how much horsepower is required for every horizontal speed, $V$, at sea level.

There is a very simple method of obtaining corrected curves for any desired altitude above sea level. According to the above formulas, both $V$ and horsepower required are inversely proportional to $\sqrt{\rho}$. At high altitude, therefore, both $V$ and horsepower required are larger than at sea level by the factor $\sqrt{\rho_0/\rho}$. Thus the curve for horsepower required at various speeds at higher altitudes is obtained simply by stretching the sea-level curve (Fig. 43) at the ratio $\sqrt{\rho_0/\rho}$ in the directions of both abscissa and ordinate, without changing the original scale of $V$ and horsepower required along these axes. The values of $\sqrt{\rho_0/\rho}$ at various altitudes are given in Table 3 of section 5.

The slope of the curve (Fig. 43) grows with increasing $V$. This indicates that twice the speed requires more than twice the horsepower. The lower part of the curve ends at a certain minimum speed which is identical with the landing speed. Small wing loading, $W/S$, is favorable to low landing speed, as may be seen from the formula for $V$. High wing loading or small wing area favors high speed, since small $S$ reduces the drag at a time when the lift is large on account of the high speed.

### 42. Horsepower Available

The horsepower delivered by the engine with throttle open at various speeds and rpm differs from the horsepower available for overcoming the drag, because the propeller bite is not 100 per cent efficient. At high speeds, when the air has not time enough to recede from the airscrew blades, the propeller efficiency is about 80 per cent. It drops to 60 per cent or less when the engine runs at less than its rated rpm. The horsepower available may be entered into the same diagram (Fig. 43) as the horsepower required. The two curves intersect at the highest possible speed of the airplane, $V_{\text{max}}$. At lower speed the horsepower available is larger than the horsepower required, and the difference between them represents the *excess* horsepower available for climbing at reduced speed. Curves for hp-available must be determined for every altitude, without the help of a simple stretching process, as in the case of the required horsepower curve. The horsepower available depends on various factors such as engine efficiency, oxygen content of the air, etc.

### 43. Rate of Climb and Ceiling

The rate at which an airplane is able to climb is closely related to the excess horsepower, that is, the difference between the power available and that required for level flight. The excess horsepower times 550 is the rate of work in ft lbs/sec available for climbing, and determines the rate of climb:

$$\text{velocity of climb in ft/sec} = \frac{\text{excess hp} \times 550}{\text{weight}}.$$

The excess horsepower varies with the forward velocity, $V$, as seen in Fig. 43. The best rate of climb is obtained at the particular forward speed at which the excess horsepower is greatest. The maximum value of the excess horsepower as well as the forward speed at which it occurs vary with the altitude. The altitude at which the airplane is still able to climb 100 ft per minute is called the *service ceiling*. The theoretical maximum altitude, or *absolute ceiling*, is reached when the maximum value of the excess power is zero.

*Example:* An airplane weighing 5000 lbs has a drag of 500 lbs when travelling at 150 miles/hr = 220 ft/sec. The engine develops 280 horsepower with a propeller efficiency of 75 per cent. What is the horsepower required for horizontal flight, and how large are the available horsepower, the rate of climb, and the angle of climb?

*Solution:* Horsepower required = $DV/550 = 500 \times 220/550 = 200$. Horsepower available = $280 \times 0.75 = 210$. Excess horsepower = $210 - 200 = 10 = 330,000$ ft lbs/min. Rate of climb = $330,000/\text{weight} = 66$ ft/min. Since $\sin \Theta$ is the ratio of vertical by horizontal velocity, we obtain $\sin \Theta = 1/200$. For this small angle, $\sin \Theta$ equals $\Theta$ in radians, $\Theta = 0.286°$.

## 44. The Best Gliding Angle and Range

Fig. 44 shows the force diagram for an airplane gliding down with speed $V$. The weight, $W$, is counterbalanced by the wind force, $F$.

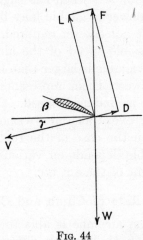

Fig. 44

The latter is the resultant of the lift at right angles to $V$ and the drag parallel to $V$. A chosen gliding angle, $\gamma$, requires a definite lift/drag ratio, namely

$$L/D = C_L/C_D = \cotg \gamma.$$

The angle $\alpha$ is the sum of $\gamma$ and $\beta$, where $\beta$ is the angle between chord and horizontal.

In order to find the best (= least) gliding angle, $\gamma_{min}$, one first has to consult the characteristic *wing* curve for the maximum value of $C_L/C_D$. The maximum occurs at a certain angle, $\alpha$, which in turn requires certain values of $C_L$ and $C_D$. Adding the parasite $C_D$, which is the same for all angles of attack, to the wing $C_D$ previously found, one obtains the drag coefficient, $C_D$, of the airplane; the latter, together with the lift coefficient, $C_L$, previously found, yields the best gliding angle according to the formula cotg $\gamma = C_L/C_D$.

Maximum *range* of an airplane in horizontal flight requires an angle of attack at which the propeller work per unit of path has minimum value. The work per unit of path equals the thrust and the drag. Maximum range is obtained, therefore, when the drag has minimum value compatible with lift equalling the weight. Since

$$D = C_D(\tfrac{1}{2}\rho V^2)S \quad \text{and} \quad L = W = C_L(\tfrac{1}{2}\rho V^2)S,$$

one has $D = C_D(W/C_L)$. Minimum $D$ belongs to maximum $C_L/C_D$. The corresponding angle of attack is the same as the angle $\alpha$ which yields the best gliding angle $\gamma$.

### 45. Stall

Many fatal accidents have been caused by stalls immediately after the take-off when the altitude was not high enough to save the craft by a quick dive. *Stalling* occurs when the plane runs into a strong upward air current producing a large angle of attack which causes the streamline flow on the upper surface of the wing first to reverse and then to turn into turbulent flow. Turbulence increases the drag and reduces the lift so much that the plane falls down due to lack of speed, usually in a slightly tilted-down position. Speed may be recovered by nosing down straight into the upward current so as to regain normal angle of attack and streamline flow. Afterward the plane may be pulled into horizontal flight again. The trouble is that the stall may occur 100 feet above the ground, whereas the dive requires a margin of 101 feet, so that the plane will crash just one foot too soon.

A remarkable reduction of the accident curve has been achieved by automatic warning devices which allow the pilot to take the necessary counter-measures in time. One device consists of a vane projecting from the leading edge of the wing; as soon as the flow begins to reverse the vane moves upward, closes a switch, and flashes a warning light or sounds a horn. Another model uses the change of dynamic pressure of the reversed flow to suck up a diaphragm which closes an electric switch and gives the warning signal.

### 46. Spiral and Tail-Spin

Stalling is often followed by a tail-spin and ends in a crash on the ground if the pilot does not recover level flight before it is too late.

Geometrically, a spiral and a spin differ only in that a spiral is a vertical screw of small pitch and large radius, whereas the spin is a vertical screw of large pitch and small radius. From the aerodynamic point of view, however, they represent two quite different modes of motion.

The *spiral* may be considered as a slight modification of ordinary rectilinear flight with a slow change of direction and altitude. The relative wind still hits the plane head on, and the angle of attack of the wing is almost the same as in horizontal flight, that is, $\alpha$ is near the value of maximum lift. The angle of bank is slight because the radius of curvature is large, and only small centrifugal forces are involved. When returning to level rectilinear flight the pilot has simply to release the rudder and the ailerons, and to pitch up the plane into horizontal position.

The spin or *tail-spin* may be compared with the motion of a horizontal airscrew parachuting down. Suppose the airplane has stalled and begins to fall, with nose tilted down a few degrees from horizontal. During the fall the wind hits the wing from below at a large angle of attack, almost 90°. Suppose now that the falling airplane is allowed to rotate freely about a fixed vertical axis through the center of gravity. It then will start to spin about the vertical axis especially if the ailerons are displaced in opposite directions, so that the wing represents a kind of two-blade propeller. Without a fixed axis holding the spinning airplane on a vertical downward path, the center of gravity will describe a downward spiral of small radius and large pitch (replacing the former vertical path along the fixed axis) even if the ailerons are kept neutral. The windmill torque sustaining the spin is caused by the dissymmetry of the wind forces on the right and left wing if the wing has dihedral and rake, and is banked slightly.

In order to pull out of a tail-spin the pilot must apply the controls in just the opposite way than expected at first sight. Since he is falling rapidly, he may be tempted to pull the elevator so as to nose up and return to level flight. Tilting up during the spin, however, would only increase the already large angle of attack with respect to the almost vertical relative wind, resulting in violent burbling on the upper wing surface and complete loss of control. If instead the pilot pushes the elevator so as to nose down, the angle of attack will be reduced, burbling will stop, and the airplane will go into a smooth dive. It then may be pulled out of the dive in the regular fashion by nosing up gently.

# Chapter VII

# The Propeller

### 47. The Propeller as Airfoil

The first airscrews were made of crude wooden spars. They were soon discarded in favor of laminated wood propellers, some of which are still in use in small private transports and military training planes. Large planes require a more resistant medium, such as steel. Steel props had to be hollow, however, to reduce their weight, in spite of their high cost of construction. A new development began with the introduction of light and strong aluminum alloys, brought to perfection by the present dural propeller with adjustable pitch by means of hydraulic or electric control from the cockpit.

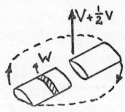

FIG. 45

A propeller blade may be considered as an airfoil which, instead of travelling forward, rotates about a fixed axis (Fig. 45). There is a marked difference, however, between wing and blade. A wing has approximately the same chord direction all along the span, apart from an occasional small twist. A propeller blade, on the other hand, is twisted so that the blade surface near the shaft is almost parallel to the shaft, whereas near the tip the blade surface is set at a flat angle of pitch with respect to the plane of rotation. The twist is introduced to provide for a constant angle of attack of the *relative wind* along the whole span, according to the following explanation.

Let us divide the blade into small slices or *blade elements*.* One of these elements will be found between the distance $r$ and $r+dr$ from the axis so as to have thickness $dr$. The blade element has two sur-

---

\* Blade element theory of Drzewiecky.

faces similar to the profile of a wing, but the "span" is only $dr$ (compare with Fig. 45). The element describes a circular path of length $2\pi r$ with velocity $w = 2\pi rn$ if $n$ is the number of revolutions per unit of time. At the same time, however, the blade and all its elements are driven forward with velocity $V$ parallel to the shaft, that is, at right angles to the circular velocity $w = 2\pi rn$. The relative wind felt by the blade element should therefore be the vector sum of the two perpendicular vectors $V$ and $w$. In fact, however, a rotating propeller produces a *slipstream* behind it, even when the airplane is at rest. If the slipstream velocity is called $v$, the rotating blade, as long as it does not travel forward, finds itself in a headwind of zero value and in a slipstream of magnitude $v$ in back of it. The average of zero and $v$ is $\frac{1}{2}v$. When the blade travels forward with speed $V$, the average headwind becomes as large as $V + \frac{1}{2}v$. The total relative wind felt by a blade element at distance $r$ from the shaft thus is the vector sum of $V + \frac{1}{2}v$ and $w = 2\pi rn$. As the two vectors are perpendicular, their sum is

$$V' = \sqrt{(V + \tfrac{1}{2}v)^2 + w^2} = \text{relative wind,}$$
$$v = \text{slipstream,} \quad w = 2\pi rn = \text{circular velocity.}$$

The direction of the relative wind, $V'$, on the blade element may be seen from Fig. 46 for an element near the blade tip, viewed in the direc-

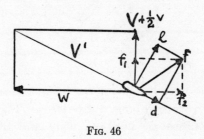

Fig. 46

tion of the blade span. The shaft points in the direction $V + \frac{1}{2}v$, and the blade element is just moving to the left; after half a revolution it will be moving to the right. During its motion the blade element is subject to lift and drag. The drag, as always, is counted parallel to the relative wind $V'$, and the lift is perpendicular to $V'$. A blade element, like a wing section, is always set at a small (almost vanishing) angle of attack between chord, $c$, and relative wind, $V'$, so as to yield a large $L/D$ ratio with

$$L \perp V' \quad \text{and} \quad c \, // \, D \, // \, V'$$

approximately. That is, the chord of the element is set almost parallel to $V'$. We now have two cases.

(1) Near the wing tip where $w \gg V$, the relative wind, $V'$, is almost parallel to the rotational velocity, $w$. Hence, also $c \mathbin{/\mkern-3mu/} V' \mathbin{/\mkern-3mu/} w$; that is, the chord is set almost within the plane of rotation, at a "small pitch."

(2) Near the shaft, where $w \ll V$, the relative wind is almost parallel to the forward velocity, $V$, so that $c \mathbin{/\mkern-3mu/} V' \mathbin{/\mkern-3mu/} V$; that is, the chord is set almost parallel to $V$ parallel to the shaft, at a large pitch.

The angle between the chord of a blade element and the plane of rotation is called the pitch of the blade element. The pitch is almost zero near the tip and almost 90° near the shaft. The pitch distribution along the span is adjusted so that the blade yields maximum thrust at the maximum number of revolutions. At a smaller number of rev/min the same blade will not yield maximum efficiency. However, the overall efficiency may be enhanced by adjusting the pitch of the blade as a whole to various rotational speeds by means of hydraulic transmission.

## 48. Propeller Efficiency

The propeller advances chiefly under the *suction* created by the blades themselves in front of them, similar to the suction above a wing. Only a small part of the thrust is due to excess pressure behind the blades. The efficiency of the propeller would be 100 per cent if the geometrical pitch of the airscrew coincided with the "effective pitch," that is, with the advance during one revolution. Actually, the effective pitch is smaller than the geometrical pitch, and the difference is known as *propeller slip*. The slip is the cause of the slipstream behind the propeller, which not only consumes energy of wasted air motion, but also exerts an additional drag on the rear parts of the airplane. Elimination or at least reduction of the slip is therefore of utmost importance.

The efficiency of the propeller rotating at a certain rate depends on the lift and drag of its blade elements. A blade element between the distances $r$ and $r + dr$ from the propeller axis has "span" $dr$, chord $c$, and area $dS = cdr$. It finds itself in relative wind $V'$. The lift, $dL$, and drag, $dD$, contributed by the element thus are

$$dL = C_L(\tfrac{1}{2}\rho V'^2)cdr, \qquad dD = C_D(\tfrac{1}{2}\rho V'^2)cdr.$$

We now turn to the question of the engine torque needed to produce a certain forward thrust of the propeller. The relation between thrust and torque may be obtained by decomposing the resultant of

$dL$ and $dD$ into one component parallel to the forward velocity $V$, called $dF_1$, and another component parallel to the circular velocity $w$, called $dF_2$ (compare with Fig. 46). The total *thrust* of the blade is obtained by summation or integration over all blade elements:

$$\text{Thrust} = \int dF_1.$$

The total *torque*, however, is obtained by multiplying each circular component by the lever arm of the respective element and summing or integrating:

$$\text{Torque} = \int r dF_2.$$

The *power consumed* in driving the airplane forward with velocity $V$ is the product of thrust and speed:

$$\text{Power consumed} = V \times \text{thrust}.$$

The *power delivered* by the torque of the shaft is the product of torque and angular velocity measured in radians. The latter is $2\pi n$ when $n$ is the number of turns per second, each turn representing $2\pi$ radians. Therefore we obtain

$$\text{Power delivered} = 2\pi n \times \text{torque}.$$

If the efficiency of the propeller were 100 percent, the two powers would be equal. In general, however, one has

$$\text{efficiency} = \frac{\text{power consumed}}{\text{power delivered}} = \frac{V \times \text{thrust}}{2\pi n \times \text{torque}}$$

which is less than 100 per cent, ranging from 80 per cent at high speeds to 60 per cent at low speeds. Those parts of the airplane which are swept over by the slipstream offer a drag increased at the ratio $(V + v)^2/V^2$ since the drag is always proportional to the square of the relative wind.

According to the same quadratic relation, the wind pressure on a fast rotating blade element increases with the *square* of the distance from the shaft. Excessive wind pressures at the blade tips are avoided by rounding the ends of the blade. This also reduces the large bending torque of the blade drag in the relative wind. The lift/drag ratio of the blade, with the "lift" supplying the major part of the propeller thrust, is increased by giving the blade a large aspect ratio, up to 8 in the case of metal blades; wooden blades cannot stand aspect ratios of more than 6.

Three- and four-blade propellers have the constructive advantage of dividing the surface area $S$ in several parts. On the other hand, if the rotating blades follow each other too closely, their efficiency is reduced by mutual interference (similar to the interference of the wings of a biplane or multiplane, section 30).

As mentioned above, the overall efficiency of a propeller may be greatly increased by allowing the pitch of the blade as a whole to be adjusted either automatically or by the pilot through hydraulic transmissions. *Adjustable pitch* permits the engine to rotate at peak efficiency with constant number of rev/min and yet to deliver variable thrust through the propeller. When a bomber with its heavy load is taking off the ground, the blades are set at low pitch so as to offer little resistance and to allow the engine to speed up to full power and maximum thrust. At high altitudes, however, the propeller is set at high pitch so as to take a bigger bite out of the rarefied air; the work of the engine is the same as on the ground due to the reduced friction of the rarefied air, and the only result of the higher pitch is an increased travelling speed at higher altitudes.

Adjustable pitch has saved many lives after sudden engine failures. A propeller without engine torque moving through the air at high speed begins to "windmill" in the wrong direction with the trailing edge of the blades ahead. This results in a large propeller drag instead of the usual thrust, and throws the airplane out of balance. If the blades can be "feathered," that is, pitched up to 90° so that their leading edges are presented to the wind, the propeller drag will decrease to almost zero, and the craft may glide down smoothly.

The *size* of the propeller is limited (a) by the clearance which has to be allowed the blades when the airplane is parked on the ground; (b) by structural reasons of avoiding excessive strains during fast rotations; (c) by the excessive drag which would occur at the blade tips if the latter should approach the speed of sound (1088 ft/sec). Near-sound speed sets up *shock waves* which consume a great amount of energy.

### 49.  The Propeller as a Gyroscope

The engine-propeller set with its rotating masses displays unexpected gyroscopic counter-torques when the axis of rotation is brought into a new direction during a change of course. If the engine rotates clockwise when viewed from the cockpit, the pilot will find that his plane tends to nose down when he steers to the right, and deviates to the left when he tries to nose down, etc. Thus when nosing down he has to apply slight right rudder in order to correct the deviation to the left. Gyroscopic deviations are rather dangerous during swift maneuvers of a high speed single-engine plane. Twin-engined and four-engined planes are free of gyroscopic forces if their engines turn in opposite directions. A single-engine plane with clockwise rotation shows deviations according to the following *clock rule*:

"The airplane deviates clockwise from the intended change of direction, unless counteracted by a counter-clockwise torque of the controls."

For example, when the pilot wants to nose up (toward 12 o'clock) the gyroscopic torque tends to yaw the plane to the right (toward 3 o'clock); therefore he has to apply left rudder (toward 9 o'clock).

The physical explanation and calculation of the gyroscopic torque rests on the fact that the angular momentum* is conserved unless acted upon by a torque. Similar to the rule of mechanics: "force

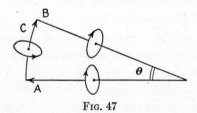

FIG. 47

equals rate of change of rectilinear momentum" ($F = dM/dt$) one has the other rule: "torque equals rate of change of angular momentum" ($T = dA/dt$). Both rules apply to every single component, the force rule to the $x$, $y$, and $z$-components of force and momentum, the torque rule to the components of torque and angular momentum about the $x$, $y$, and $z$-directions as axes of rotation. Forces and rectilinear momenta of various directions may be composed like vectors to yield a resulting force and a resulting rectilinear moment. The same applies to torques and angular momenta, when these quantities are represented as *vectors* in the direction of their axes of rotation. The rotation vector is drawn in the forward direction of a right-hand screw. An example of vector composition of torques and angular momenta, similar to the parallelogram of forces and linear momenta, is given in Fig. 47. The clockwise rotating propeller has angular momentum, $A$, illustrated by a vector in the direction of the outstretched right arm

* The angular momentum, $A$, is the product of the moment of inertia, $J$, and the angular velocity, $\omega$, so that $A = J\omega$. In the case of $n$ revolutions per unit of time, $\omega$ equals $2\pi n$, whereas $J = mR^2$, where $R$ is the radius of gyration, and $m$ is the mass of the rotating body. When all masses are condensed on the outer rim of radius $r$, the radius of gyration $R$ equals $r$. In the case of various masses, $m$, being found at various distances, $r$, from the axis, the radius of gyration is defined by the equation $R^2 = \Sigma mr^2/\Sigma m$.

of the pilot, or by an arrow or vector pointing in the forward direction of the propeller axis. The direction of the vector indicates the direction of rotation (right-hand screw), whereas the length of the vector must be proportional to the magnitude of the angular momentum, $A$. When the airplane is nosed up into the new axis direction $B$ through the pitching angle $\Theta$ the change of angular momentum from $A$ to $B$ requires the addition of an angular momentum $C$ of magnitude and direction indicated by the vector $C$ in Fig. 47, so that $\overrightarrow{A} + \overrightarrow{B} = \overrightarrow{C}$. If the angle $\Theta$ is small, one has the approximate equation $C = A\Theta$, when $\Theta$ is measured in radians. Angular momentum about the axis direction $C$ may be supplied by simultaneous application of left rudder, as though the pilot wanted to swing the nose to the left or the tail to the right. Similar considerations apply to the case of steering to the right, etc.; the result is always in accordance with the clock rule.

The magnitude of the counter-torque preventing gyroscopic deviation depends on the mass and the rotational speed of the engine-propeller set. If heavy rotating engine parts are avoided, the counter-torque remains small compared with the main control torque producing the desired change of direction. A quantitative determination may be obtained from the following fundamental law of mechanics: "The torque equals the change of angular momentum per unit of time." (This law corresponds to Newton's law for rectilinear motion: "The force equals the change of momentum per unit of time"). If the angular momentum is to be changed from $A$ to $B$ during the time $t$, the additional angular momentum needed for this purpose is $C$, and the torque producing $C$ is $C/t$. If $\Theta$ is small, $C$ equals $A\Theta$; since $A = J\omega = J2\pi n$ with $J$ = moment of inertia, one obtains

$$\text{torque} = A\Theta/t = J \cdot 2\pi n\Theta/t.$$

Let us consider a propeller of mass $m$ with blades of span $r$. If the mass were condensed at the blade tips, the moment of inertia, $J$, would be $mr^2$. Actually, the mass is more or less uniformly distributed over the span; in this case the moment of inertia is only $J = \frac{1}{3}mr^2$. Furthermore, if $n$ is the number of revolutions per unit of time, the angular velocity in radians is $\omega = 2\pi n$. The propeller thus has angular momentum

$$A = J\omega = \tfrac{1}{3}mr^2 \times 2\pi n.$$

Suppose the propeller weighs 180 lbs, has radius $r = 4$ ft, and rotates 24 times per second. The angular momentum then is 145,000 lbs ft²/sec. Suppose further that the plane is pitched up through an angle

$\Theta = 6°$ within $\frac{1}{2}$ second. This means that an additional momentum, $C = A\Theta$, must be supplied during the same time interval, that is,

$$C = 145,000(6\pi/180) = 15,120 \text{ lbs ft}^2/\text{sec.}$$

The corresponding torque is $C/t = 30,240$ ft pdls = 944 ft lbs. In order to offset gyroscopic deviation, an equal counter-torque has to be applied in the form of left rudder. If the rudder is 40 feet aft of the c.g., the force on the rudder must be 944/40 = 23.6 lbs. The example shows that the gyroscopic effect is comparatively small if the engine does not contain heavy rotating parts.

**Problem:** A propeller of weight 150 lbs rotates at 1200 rpm. The propeller diameter is 8 feet. The airplane is to be turned 20° to the right in 4 seconds. What kind of control action is needed? How large is the gyroscopic torque? How many pounds are to be applied to the control surface if the latter is 50 feet abaft the c.g.?

The idea of mounting two *counter-rotating propellers* one behind the other and driven by a single engine has been tested with apparent success by the Standard Propeller Company. The disadvantage of a complicated gearing mechanism is offset by the following aerodynamic advantages of the dual propeller: Less interference between the blades of every single propeller, so that three blades may be applied in spite of high rotational speed; elimination of the slipstream torque on the rear parts of the airplane; absence of gyroscopic torques during maneuvers; and elimination of the mechanical counter-torque on the airplane body.

# Chapter VIII

## Unconventional Types of Aircraft

### 50. Jet-propelled Craft

The ordinary propeller-driven airplane begins to lose efficiency at speeds over 450 mph because the blade tips, which rotate at a still higher speed, produce an excessive propeller drag. This effect may be eliminated by installing a jet-propulsion unit. The first jet-propelled airplane was designed by Campini and flown near Milan, Italy, in 1940. A satisfactory jet-propulsion engine has been developed by Wing Commander F. Whittle in England. After three years of flight tests, hundreds of successful flights with improved models have been made in America and England. At the present time the U. S. Army is experimenting with a twin-engined, jet-propelled fighter of high speed and high ceiling; details are not available for military reasons.

The Italian jet-plane is driven by an ordinary airscrew at low altitudes, and the jet is applied only for high-altitude flight at high speeds. The air enters at the nose of the airplane under the impact pressure of the forward motion. A rotational air pump driven by the engine presses the air through a tunnel having contractions and bulges; here the air is mixed with the exhaust gases to increase the temperature. The compressed air then is supplied with fuel. The exhaust of the combustion chamber leads into a nozzle having a variable conic orifice. The jet emerges with very high speed and supplies a powerful thrust. The jet reaction may be compared with that of a stiff arm repelling itself from a succession of solid walls. This effect is added to the *rocket effect*, according to which a body of mass $M$ and velocity $V$ increases its forward momentum, $MV$, at the expense of the momentum, $mv$, ejected to the rear with velocity $v$ in the form of masses $m$. The rocket operates *in vacuo* ("space ship"), whereas the jet uses both rocket action and the "stiffness" of the opposing atmosphere. Jet-propulsion is particularly efficient at speeds over 400 mph during the critical moments of an air engagement.

The German *robot bomb* is a jet-powered and gyro-controlled aerial torpedo. After having flown over a pre-determined distance the motor shuts off automatically, and the bomb glides down. The schematic picture (frontispiece) shows the warhead containing approximately 1000 kg of explosives, the light alloy nose containing a compass, the launching rail, the fuel tank and two wirebound spherical bottles for compressed air, a grill with fuel-injection jets, and the impulse suction engine, also the air-driven gyros actuating the pneumatic servo units which operate the rudder and elevator. Like all jet-propelled craft, the aerial torpedo does not require high-grade gasoline, and its overall price is estimated at not more than $4000, which makes large-scale production possible.

The jet bomb can be aimed at a large area only because of wind variations. Allowing for a wind of $\pm$ 30 miles/hr and a bomb travelling at 300 miles/hr the margin of error would be 30/300 = 1/10 radian, or 6°. At a distance of 100 miles this means a spread of 10 miles, so that a big city can and is being bombed effectively as this is written. In addition, it seems that the jet bomb contains a highly sensitive instrument which in conjunction with the compass compensates automatically for wind drift. Range can be controlled by a time device. The barometric pressure may be assumed to be fairly constant over the distance of 100 miles, so that altitude may be controlled by a barometer. The specifications of the jet bomb according to the British press are: Overall length 25' $4\frac{1}{3}''$, wing span 16', length of fuselage 21' 10", maximum width of fuselage 2' $8\frac{1}{2}''$. The robot is launched from a ramp or from a hydraulic catapult.

### 51. The Helicopter

Winged airplanes are ideal vehicles for long-distance travel at high speed, for gliding, for diving, climbing, and other maneuvers. The airplane "soars like an eagle and swoops like a swallow," but it cannot hover motionless over an object like a bug or rise straight into the air. The need for a long airstrip may be overcome by catapulting, which, however, does not solve the problem of landing on rough ground. The idea of using an auxiliary airscrew rotating about a vertical axis for the take-off and landing has often been tried but has never succeeded. Only the radical step of eliminating the wing altogether and replacing it by a large horizontal airscrew (rotor) has met with practical success. There are two types of wingless aircraft. The rotor of the autogiro is used for the take-off and for sustentation, and

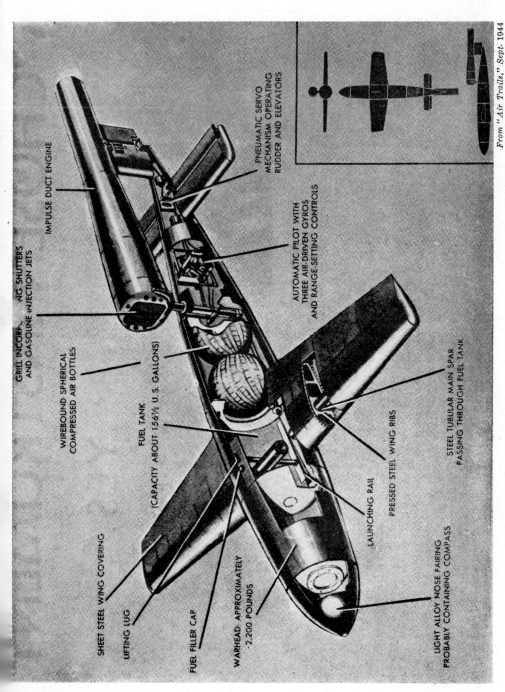

IMPULSE DUCT ENGINE

PNEUMATIC SERVO
MECHANISM OPERATING
RUDDER AND ELEVATORS

GRILL INCORP... NG SHUTTERS
AND GASOLINE INJECTION JETS

AUTOMATIC PILOT WITH
THREE AIR-DRIVEN GYROS
AND RANGE-SETTING CONTROLS

WIREBOUND SPHERICAL
COMPRESSED AIR BOTTLES

FUEL TANK
(CAPACITY ABOUT 156½ U.S. GALLONS)

STEEL TUBULAR MAIN SPAR
PASSING THROUGH FUEL TANK

LAUNCHING RAIL

PRESSED STEEL WING RIBS

SHEET STEEL WING COVERING

LIFTING LUG

FUEL FILLER CAP

WARHEAD: APPROXIMATELY
2,200 POUNDS

LIGHT ALLOY NOSE FAIRING
PROBABLY CONTAINING COMPASS

*From "Air Trails," Sept. 1944*

Cross-section cutaway drawing of most common Nazi flying bomb. It is 25 ft. 4 in. long and is made mostly from pressed steel. (British Information Service, Acme.)

an additional, vertical screw provides the propulsion. The helicopter (from *helico* = spiral, and *pter* = bird) derives both lift and thrust from the rotor, and needs small auxiliary airscrews only for reasons of stability and control.

The torque exerted by the engine on the big rotor is accompanied by an equal counter-torque tending to spin the craft in the opposite direction. In order to avoid the spin, earlier models of the helicopter were equipped with twin rotors revolving in opposite directions. The new helicopter of Sikorsky contains only a single large, three-bladed rotor. This has the advantage of simplified power transmission directly from the engine to the rotor hub, and also reduces the dimen-

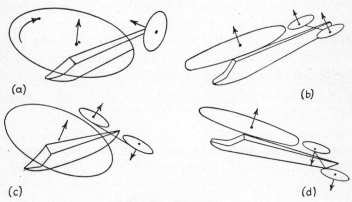

(a)  (b)  (c)  (d)

FIG. 48.   Helicopter.

a. Rudder rotor counteracts torque.
b. Trimming rotors lift tail, craft flies forward.
c. Trimming rotors bank craft for turn.
d. Trimming rotors depress tail, craft flies backward.

sions of the craft. The counter-torque of the big rotor on the body is cancelled by a small auxiliary propeller at the tail rotating about a lateral axis (Fig. 48). The blade pitch of the *tail screw* can be changed by the pilot to provide a variable lateral thrust similar to that of a rudder. Two small *trimming screws*, or outboard rotors, with vertical axes are placed on the right and left of the rear end of the helicopter. When the pitch of the two trimming screws is increased simultaneously, the rear end rises, and the axis of the main rotor leans forward. In this position the rotor provides a forward thrust in addition to lift. When the pitch of the trimming screws is reversed, the rear goes down, and the main rotor now provides a backward thrust. On the other hand, when the two trimming screws are given opposite pitch, they produce bank like the ailerons of the ordinary airplane. The craft thus is able to rise vertically, descend, travel forward, sidewise, and backward, to bank, and to hover motionless over an object. It may become the ideal type for the "Sunday-flyer" after the war, although its operation requires great skill.

The auxiliary screws are coupled to the main rotor by mechanical transmissions. If the engine fails, the craft glides down vertically; the main rotor revolves without engine power like a windmill, and the auxiliary screws drives by the mechanical transmissions, so that control is maintained.

The latest Sikorsky helicopter has a main rotor 36 feet in diameter and a $7\frac{1}{2}$-foot rudder screw. It is 38 feet long and weighs 2,400 lbs. The main rotor revolves at a constant speed of about 270 rpm, which corresponds to a blade-tip velocity of 350 mph and explains the large lift of the rotor. The blade pitch is adjustable during flight. In recent tests the helicopter has attained a forward speed of 82 miles/hr and has climbed to an altitude of 5,000 feet.

## 52.  The Autogiro

In contrast to the helicopter, the forward thrust of the autogiro is furnished by an ordinary propeller at the rear end, whereas the lift is supplied by a large rotor free-wheeling in the wind without engine

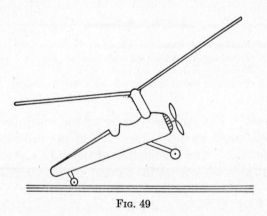

Fig. 49

power (except during the take-off). The rotor axis is not in a fixed position with respect to the body, but is hinged to a pivot so that the rotor axis may be tilted in any desired direction. In neutral position the rotor axis points through the center of gravity of the craft. When tilted, the axis direction is displaced, so that the upward thrust of the rotor at the same time exerts a torque about the c.g. The pilot thus may turn the craft in any desired direction.

The rotor blades are hinged to the vertical shaft and may flap up and down freely between certain limits. Their position of balance in flight is parallel to the resultant of the vertical upward force of lift and the radial centrifugal force. The blades are thus tilted up slightly and describe a flat cone opening upward. Since both lift and centrifugal force are proportional to the square of the blade-tip velocity, the angle of the cone is the same at all rotational speeds. The rotor blades change their pitch automatically under increased wind pressure, so that sudden air bumps are smoothed out automatically.

In order to understand why the main rotor revolves in flight without engine power, let us consider a horizontal wind, $V$, acting on a two-blade rotor with vertical axis at the moment when the horizontal blade spans happen to be at right angles to the wind. One blade then has the same position in the wind as the wing of an airplane in horizontal flight, whereas the other blade is in reverse position, so that the wind hits the rear edge first. Both blades tend to yield to the wind, and to rotate in opposite directions; the second blade, in reverse position, wins because the wind drag on a reversed wing is larger than on a wing in regular position. Thus the rotor begins to windmill in the horizontal wind. The leading edges of both blades point in the direction of the *rotational* velocity; both blades will supply lift. The magnitude of the lift supplied by a blade element is proportional to the square of the *relative* wind, which is the resultant of rotational and forward velocity. The blade tips have a rotational velocity of 240 mph, whereas the craft has a forward speed of about 60 mph.

It may seem strange at first sight that the blade tips should have a velocity far surpassing the forward speed of the craft, although the relative wind produced by the forward speed is the only cause of the rotation. The explanation is that the wind torque, which keeps the blades rotating, is attacking at the *center of drag* of each blade. The latter may be located three times closer to the shaft than the blade tip. The center of drag will never rotate faster than the forward speed, even in the most favorable case that the drag acts only on the blade in reverse wing position and is negligible on the opposite blade in regular wing position. This still would permit the blade tips to have a rotational velocity three times the forward speed. The lift of the rotor is produced mainly near the fast-moving blade tips, since the lift of a blade element is proportional to the *square* of the relative wind.

This also explains the large lift of the rotor, in spite of the small blade surface compared with the wing surface of an ordinary airplane.

As long as the craft is moving forward under the thrust of the rear propeller, the rotor keeps spinning around automatically and yields the lift sustaining the craft. If the forward motion should stop due to engine failure, the rotor will act as a vertical windmill, and the autogiro will parachute down gently.

A special technique of "jumping" off the ground has been developed with the Pitcairn autogiro. The rotor blades are first set at zero pitch so as to offer minimum drag; they are brought into rapid rotation by the engine. The pitch is then increased and the power switched off. The rotor continues to revolve rapidly under its own inertia, producing a more than normal lift, so that the craft rises into the air. At the same time power is applied to the rear propeller, to produce forward speed. In the meantime the rotor settles down to its normal speed of about 170 rpm.

The autogiro is controlled by an ordinary tail with rudder and elevator. Additional control may be obtained by shifting the rotor axis away from the center of gravity. Both autogiro and helicopter are designed for short trips without prepared landing strips.

## 53. Gliders

The conventional glider is an ordinary airplane without engine and propeller, which relies for sustentation on the effect of rising air currents. The craft glides down relative to a rising current without losing altitude. It is launched into the air by catapulting or towing with an automobile.

*Tail-less gliders* consisting of only a wing of large aspect ratio have been built and flown by the Horton brothers in Germany. Stability of the all-wing glider is secured by a considerable dihedral angle and sweepback. The pilot controls roll, pitch, and yaw from a small cockpit located within the wing root. Three flaps are hinged to the trailing edge of right and left wings and serve as elevators and ailerons. An additional flap on the leading edge of either wing increases the maneuverability of the craft. Turns are achieved by banking. The tail-less glider has stayed in the air for nine and a half hours with the pilot in a fairly comfortable kneeling-lying position.

An all-wing airplane without fuselage and tail, driven by twin engines at the rear, has been developed by the Northrup Aircraft Company. Due to the lack of parasite drag the craft develops a speed of more than 400 miles per hour, and hundreds of successful flights have been made.

## 54. Automatic Pilot

The automatic pilot, which has become an indispensable standard piece of equipment in big bombers, represents an engineering feat of the first order. It is a perfection of the hydraulic pilot which has been used for more than ten years in commercial transport planes and certain combat types. The Minneapolis Honeywell C-1 pilot is based exclusively on electronic amplification of the minute torques exerted by two highly sensitive gyroscopes. In order to hold the airplane in a definite attitude relative to three fixed axes in space, one needs only *two* fixed gyro axes. Indeed, if the vertical axis is fixed, the longitudinal and lateral axes are both within the plane of the horizon, and one azimuth angle determines the position of both of them. The two gyros applied in the automatic pilot are, the *directional stabilizer* or horizontal gyro (whose axis is horizontal and whose disk is vertical) pointing in the longitudinal direction, and the *vertical gyro* spinning about a vertical axis and controlling pitch and roll. The two gyros are the same as those already used in the instrument panel as directional gyro and artificial horizon.

The movements of the airplane about the spinning rotors are picked up electronically and amplified so as to actuate the three *servo units* which control the elevator, the rudder, and the ailerons. These servo units are located not far from their respective control surfaces. This has the advantage of comparatively short transmission cables which do not contract and expand so much under variations of temperature and are less exposed to damage under combat conditions. Several cases are known in which the manual controls were shot out of action, and the plane was brought home safely by the automatic pilot, whose servo units still responded to the adjustment of the gyros.

During the few seconds of a bombing run the autopilot offers an absolutely stable platform which is vital for precision bombing at high altitudes. At 30,000 feet a deviation of 1°, or 1/57 radian, would mean missing the target by 30,000/57 or about 500 feet.

# Chapter IX

# Instruments of Navigation

## 55. The Amount Group

If the pilot were led only by his natural sense of equilibrium he never would find his way through fog and darkness, nor could he keep his plane in balance on a straight horizontal course. A glance at the instrument board with its array of dials and pointers must give him all the information necessary to keep his plane in equilibrium, to reach his goal, or to carry out his mission of destruction. The following report on aircraft instruments omits all reference to the engine and describes only the principal instruments of *navigation*. These are divided in two groups. The *amount group* determines the altitude relative to a zero level, the direction of flight relative to the geographic or magnetic NS-direction, and the angles of pitch and bank relative to the horizon. The *rate group* of instruments measures the rate of travel that is, the speed, the rate of ascent and descent, and the rate of turn when changing course or maneuvering.

(1) **The altimeter.** Altitudes are determined indirectly with the help of a barometer. The pressure is related to the elevation above zero-level according to the barometer formula

$$p/p_0 = \exp(-h\mu/RT)$$

where $\mu$ is the apparent molecular weight of the air ($\mu = 28.9$), $h$ is the height above zero-level where the pressure is $p_0$, $T$ is the absolute temperature, and $R$ is the universal gas constant. When $h$ is measured in cm or feet, $R$ must be expressed in gram-cm or foot-pounds, respectively. The inversion of the last equation with $R = 1.98$ calories per degree centigrade yields the height above zero-level:

$$h = 221.15 \times T \log(p_0/p).$$

$h$ is obtained in feet when $T$ is measured in absolute degrees centigrade; log is Brigg's logarithm.

The barometer determines the altitude above sea-level, above the landing field, or above any other zero level. The *absolute* altitude of the airplane above the ground may be determined by electrostatic, sonic, or radio methods. *Electrostatic* altitude measurements are based on the fact that the capacity of a condenser decreases with increasing distance between the plates. One plate is mounted on the underside of the airplane, the other plate is represented by the ground. The electrostatic method determines altitudes up to 100 feet with sufficient accuracy to protect the plane from crashing on the ground or on a mountainside. The *sonic* method determines the absolute height by measuring the time interval of a sound signal travelling to the ground and returning to the airplane. The *radio* method uses the interference of radio waves reflected from the ground.

(2) **The Compass.** The ordinary compass needle behaves too erratically under perturbations to be of much use in flight. The airplane compass has to be *aperiodic*. It contains a magnetic needle attached to a compass card floating horizontally on a damping fluid. The instrument measures the horizontal component of the earth's magnetic field. The floating compass is worthless, however, during turns, just when an exact determination of the horizontal direction is needed most, since the liquid surface goes into a banked position.

A new method of measuring the horizontal magnetic field without interference of inertia is effected by the *flux-gate compass*. When a flat, circular coil in vertical position rotates about the vertical diameter, the magnetic flux through the coil serving as a "gate" increases and decreases periodically. The largest flux change per second occurs when the flux itself changes from positive to negative, that is, when the vertical coil passes through the NS-direction. The induction current is zero when the vertical coil is in the EW-position. When the brushes of the commutator are set to draw current in the EW-direction of the coil, the amperemeter will not show any current. If the whole instrument is turned into a new direction to the right, the ammeter will indicate "positive" current; an opposite turn of the instrument will produce "negative" current in the ammeter, so that the latter serves as a compass, measuring deviation from the original EW-direction of the brushes.

However, a change of current through the ammeter is also observed when the instrument is tipped over, with the axis of rotation deviating from vertical. The corresponding change of current due to pitch and roll could be mistaken as due to a change of course. It is necessary, therefore, to keep the rotational axis of the coil stationary in a vertical position, irrespective of the motion of the airplane itself. This is achieved by the *Bendix* gyro-flux-gate compass with its electrically driven gyroscope rotating at the rate of more than 10,000 rpm. The instrument is mounted in the tail, and its tiny induction currents are amplified and sent to the ammeter at the instrument board. The compass has a remarkable stability and accuracy during maneuvers, and may be used within a few degrees of the magnetic pole of the earth, where ordinary compass needles are quite unreliable.

(3) **The turn indicator,** or directional gyro, serves as an auxiliary *mechanical* compass, independent of the earth's magnetic field. As the gyro axis is set parallel to the span, the plane of rotation points in the direction of travel. The frame supporting the horizontal gyro axis is allowed to turn about a vertical axis (Fig. 50). The wheel persists

Fig. 50

in the original direction of travel and acts as a compass during a change of course. When the turn is completed, the wheel may be reset in the new direction of travel ready to indicate the next change of course.

(4) **The artificial horizon,** or flight indicator, contains a gyro with a persistent vertical axis. The horizontally rotating disk is optically projected as a horizontal bar on a dial. The latter carries an angular scale on its circumference and a horizontal wing symbol at the center. When the airplane, together with the dial, assumes a new orientation, the wing symbol shows the exact position of the airplane with respect to the horizontal bar. Fig. 51 shows the dial during climb, dive, right bank, and combination of right bank and dive during a downward spiral.

The gyro axis must turn freely in all directions, or rather, the supporting framework must be capable of turning in all directions without interfering with the fixed direction of the gyro axis. This is achieved by mounting the vertical gyro axis in a first frame which may turn about a horizontal axis within a second frame. The latter is held by a third frame, to allow the second frame to turn about a vertical axis (Fig. 52).

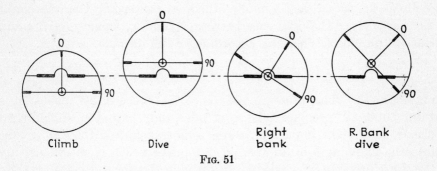

Climb Dive Right bank R. Bank dive

FIG. 51

A combination of the artificial horizon and the turn indicator may be used to keep the airplane *automatically* on a fixed horizontal course by electronic amplification of the gyro reaction to directional changes of the airplane axes. The automatic pilot, or "robot plane" is rather

FIG. 52

dangerous in rough weather, however. Heavy wing loads and large strains on the controls on its undeviating straight course might result in serious injury to the airplane. On the other hand, the automatic pilot takes over the manual control and furnishes an absolutely stable platform during the critical moments of a bombing run.

## 56. The Rate Group

(1) **The air-speed indicator.** A direct method for determining the air speed or relative wind would consist in projecting a windmill (anemometer) into the undisturbed air in front of the plane. Indirect methods are based on Bernoulli's theorem concerning the relation of air speed, $V$, to the difference between dynamic impact-pressure and static atmospheric pressure, according to the formula

$$p - p_0 = \tfrac{1}{2}\rho V^2/g; \ \ \text{hence} \ \ V = \sqrt{2\tfrac{1}{2}(p - p_0)g/\rho},$$

of section 5. The pressure difference is observed by means of a Pitot tube. A pressure inlet protrudes right into the undisturbed atmosphere. The impact pressure, $p$, is transmitted through a tube into the diaphragm of an aneroid barometer which is surrounded by the static pressure $p_0$. The barometer indicates the difference, $p - p_0$, from which $V$ is obtained according to the above formula. It is not possible to use a direct V-scale on the barometer because of the variability of the density, $\rho$. Values of $\rho$ for various altitudes may be taken from table 3, section 5. The tube must be heated electrically to avoid stoppage by ice formation.

(2) **The rate-of-climb indicator (vertical speed indicator).** The diaphragm of an aneroid barometer is sealed into an air-tight chamber of constant pressure, $p$, whereas the interior of the diaphragm communicates with the outside pressure, $p_0$. If $p_0$ rises during a dive, the diaphragm expands against the constant pressure, $p$, in the chamber. However, if the diaphragm has a tiny outlet into the chamber, the pressure difference, $p - p_0$, levels out in the course of time. If the dive continues, the time is too short for a complete adjustment of the chamber pressure to the external pressure. Instead, one obtains a *constant pressure difference* proportional to the *rate* of descent, although both $p_0$ and $p$ increase during the descent. The difference, $p - p_0$, is indicated by the barometer. When the airplane resumes level flight, the pressure difference disappears, although with a certain time lag. A pressure difference of opposite sign develops during a climb and is proportional to the rate of climb.

The vertical speed indicator is an important supplement of the altimeter. The latter, too, indicates every change of altitude during ascent or descent. However, the scale of the altimeter covers the whole range of elevations from sea-level to many thousands of feet on a single scale, and is not likely to indicate small changes of altitude with great accuracy; in particular, it does not show directly the *rate* of change. The rate-of-climb indicator, on the other hand, registers small pressure differences between diaphragm and vessel during ascent and descent.

(3) **The rate-of-turn and bank indicator.** The airplane has to be banked during a turn to avoid sideslipping (inward) or skidding (outward). The proper angle of bank corresponding to a chosen *rate* of turn is identical with the angle of deviation from the vertical of a free pendulum, and also with the angle of bank of a liquid surface carried on the turning airplane. The free pendulum is too unstable to serve as a reliable bank indicator. An aperiodic bank indicator consists of a glass ball half filled with a viscous fluid, whose surface coincides with the equator of the glass ball in straight level flight. If the airplane is banked correctly during a turn, the liquid surface ought again to coincide with the equator. The pilot therefore has the task of keeping coincidence all the time, in straight flight as well as during a turn.

FIG. 53

The *rate of turn* may be determined by the counter-force to any change of direction of a gyroscopic axis. A gyro may rotate about the lateral airplane axis so that the rotating disk points in the direction of travel. The frame holding the gyro axis must be able to rotate about the longitudinal airplane axis so that the gyro axis may go into a banked position (Fig. 53). Suppose the gyro rotates in a clockwise direction, as viewed from the left wing tip. If the airplane turns to the right, the horizontal gyro axis tends to bank down on the right, according to the clock rule discussed in Section 49. The counter-torque needed to prevent this deviation is proportional to the angular velocity, that is, to the *rate* of turn. The counter-torque may be measured by a torsion scale. The latter may be adjusted so that the scale pointer moves just into the proper banking angle corresponding to the rate of turn; the pointer remains perpendicular to the equator of the glass ball if the airplane has assumed the correct banking angle.

# Appendix

# Nomenclature of Aeronautics*

**Aerodynamics:**  The branch of dynamics that treats of the motion of air and other gaseous fluids and of the forces acting on solids in motion relative to such fluids.

**Aerodynamic center of wing section:**  A point located on or near the chord of the mean line approximately one-quarter of the chord length aft of the leading edge, and about which the moment coefficient is practically constant.

**Aileron:**  A hinged or movable portion of an airplane wing, the primary function of which is to impress a rolling motion on the airplane.  It is usually part of the trailing edge of a wing.

**Aircraft:**  Any weight-carrying device designed to be supported by the air, either by buoyancy or by dynamic action.

**Airfoil:**  Any surface, such as an airplane wing, aileron, or rudder, designed to obtain reaction from the air through which it moves.

**Airfoil profile:**  The outline of an airfoil section.

**Airfoil section:**  A cross-section of an airfoil parallel to the plane of symmetry or to a specified reference plane.

**Airplane:**  A mechanically driven, fixed-wing aircraft, heavier than air, which is supported by the dynamic reaction of the air against its wings.

**Airspeed:**  The speed of an aircraft relative to the air.

**Altimeter:**  An instrument that measures the elevation of an aircraft above a given datum plane.

**Angle:**

*Aileron angle:*  The angular displacement of an aileron from its neutral position.  It is positive when the trailing edge of the aileron is below the neutral position.

*Blade angle:*  The acute angle between the chord of a section of a propeller or of a rotary wing system, and a plane perpendicular to the axis of rotation.

*Dihedral angle:*  The acute angle between a line perpendicular to symmetry and the projection of the wing axis on a plane perpendicular to the longitudinal axis of the airplane.  If the wing axis is not approximately a straight line, the angle is measured from the projection of a line joining the intersection of the wing axis with the plane of symmetry and the aerodynamic center of the half-wing on either side of the plane of symmetry.

*Downwash angle:*  The angle through which an airstream is deflected by

* Extracts from Report No. 474 by the National Advisory Committee for Aeronautics.

107

any lifting surface. It is measured in a plane parallel to the plane of symmetry.

*Drift angle:* The horizontal angle between the longitudinal axis of an aircraft and its path relative to the ground.

*Gliding angle:* The angle between the flight path during a glide and a horizontal axis fixed relative to the air.

*Minimum gliding angle:* The acute angle between the horizontal and the most nearly horizontal path along which an airplane can descend steadily in still air when the propeller is producing no thrust.

**Angle of attack:** The acute angle between a reference line in a body and the line of the relative wind direction projected on a plane containing the reference line and parallel to the plane of symmetry.

**Angle of attack for infinite aspect ratio:** The angle of attack at which an airfoil produces a given lift coefficient in a two-dimensional flow. Also called "effective angle of attack."

**Angle of incidence:** Same as "angle of wing setting." In British terminology the angle of incidence is equivalent to the American term "angle of attack."

**Angle of pitch** (aircraft): The acute angle between two planes defined as follows: One plane includes the lateral axis of the aircraft and the direction of the relative wind; the other plane includes the lateral axis and the longitudinal axis. The angle is positive when the nose of the aircraft is above the direction of the relative wind. (In normal flight the angle of pitch is the angle between the longitudinal axis and the direction of the relative wind.)

**Angle of roll or angle of bank:** The angle through which an aircraft must be rotated about its longitudinal axis in order to bring its lateral axis into the horizontal plane. The angle is positive when the left side is higher than the right.

**Angle of yaw:** The acute angle between the direction of the relative wind and the plane of symmetry of an aircraft. The angle is positive when the aircraft turns to the right.

**Area, equivalent flat-plate:** The area of a square flat plate, normal to the direction of motion, which offers the same amount of resistance to motion as the body or combination of bodies under consideration.

**Area, measurement of** (performance calculations):

*Control-surface area, trailing:* The area of a trailing control surface is the area of the actual outline projected on the plane of the surface, except that any portion of the movable surface lying forward of the hinge axis and within the fixed surface is included in the fixed surface. Auxiliary or paddle-type balance surfaces shielded by and lying outside of the fixed surface are not included in the area of either the fixed or the movable surfaces.

*Horizontal tail area:* The horizontal tail area is measured in the same manner as the wing area, that is, with no deduction for the area blanketed by the fuselage, such blanketed area being bounded within the fuselage by lateral straight lines that connect the intersections of the leading and trailing edges of the stabilizer with the sides of the fuselage, the fairings and fillets being ignored.

*Vertical tail area:* The area of the actual outline of the rudder and the fin projected in the vertical plane, the fairings and fillets being ignored.

*Wing area:* Wing area is measured from the projection of the actual outline on the plane of the chords, without deduction for area blanketed by fuselage or nacelles. That part of the area, so determined, which lies within the fuselage or nacelles is bounded by two lateral lines that connect the intersections of the leading and trailing edges with the fuselage or nacelle, ignoring fairings and fillets. For the purpose of calculating area, a wing is considered to extend without interruption through the fuselage and nacelles. Unless otherwise stated, wing area always refers to total area including ailerons.

**Artificial horizon:** (1) A device that indicates the attitude of an aircraft with respect to the true horizon. (2) A substitute for a natural horizon such as a liquid level, pendulum, or gyroscope, incorporated in a navigating instrument.

**Aspect ratio:** The ratio of the span to the mean chord of an airfoil; *i.e.*, the ratio of the square of the span to the total area of an airfoil.

*Effective aspect ratio:* The aspect ratio of an airfoil of elliptical plan form that, for the same lift coefficient, has the same induced-drag coefficient as the airfoil, or the combination of airfoils, in question.

**Atmosphere:**

*Standard:* An arbitrary atmosphere used in comparing the performance of aircraft. The standard atmosphere in use in the United States at present represents very nearly the average conditions found at latitude 40° N and is completely defined in N.A.C.A. Report No. 218.

*Standard international:* The atmosphere used as an international standard presumes for mean sea level and a temperature of 15° C, a pressure of 1,013.2 millibars, lapse rate of 6.5° C per kilometer from sea level to 11 kilometers, and thereafter a constant temperature of −56.5° C.

**Attitude:** The position of an aircraft as determined by the inclination of its axes to some frame of reference. If not otherwise specified, this frame of reference is fixed to earth.

**Autogiro:** A type of rotor plane whose support in the air is chiefly derived from airfoils rotated about an approximately vertical axis by aerodynamic forces, and in which the lift on opposite sides of the plane of symmetry is equalized by the vertical oscillation of the blades.

**Automatic pilot:** An automatic control mechanism for keeping an aircraft in level flight and on a set course. Sometimes called "gyro pilot," "mechanical pilot," or "robot pilot."

**Axes of an aircraft:** Three fixed lines of reference, usually centroidal and mutually perpendicular. The axis in the plane of symmetry, usually parallel to the axis of the propeller, is called the longitudinal axis; the axis perpendicular to this in the plane of symmetry is called the normal axis; and the third axis perpendicular to the other two is called the lateral axis. In mathematical discussions, the first of these axes, drawn from rear to front, is called the $X$ axis; the second, drawn downward, the $Z$ axis; and the third, running from left to right, the $Y$ axis.

**Balance:** A condition of steady flight in which the resultant force and moment of the airplane are zero.

*Aerodynamic balanced surface:* A control that extends on both sides of the axis of the hinge or pivot or that has auxiliary devices or extensions connected with it in such a manner as to effect a small or zero resultant moment of the air forces about the hinge axis.

*Static balanced surface:* A control surface whose center of mass is in the hinge axis.

**Bank:** The position of an airplane when its lateral axis is inclined to the horizontal. A right bank is the position with the lateral axis inclined downward to the right.

**Bank:** To incline an airplane laterally; *i.e.,* to rotate it about its longitudinal axis.

**Biplane:** An airplane with two main supporting surfaces one above the other.

**Blade element:** A portion of a propeller blade contained between the surfaces of two cylinders coaxial with the propeller cutting the propeller blades.

**Blade section:** A cross-section of a propeller blade made at any point by a plane parallel to the axis of rotation of the propeller and tangent at the centroid of the section to an arc drawn with the axis of rotation as its center.

**Boundary layer:** A layer of fluid, close to the surface of a body placed in a moving stream, in which the impact pressure is reduced as a result of the viscosity of the fluid.

**Bump:** A sudden acceleration of an aircraft caused by a region of unstable atmosphere characterized by marked local vertical components in the air currents.

**Burble:** A term designating the breakdown of the streamline flow about a body.

**Camber:** The rise of the curve of an airfoil section, usually expressed as the ratio of the curve from a straight line joining the extremities of the curve to the length of this straight line. "Upper camber" refers to the upper surface; "lower camber" to the lower surface; and "mean camber" to the mean line of the section. Camber is positive when the departure is upward, and negative when it is downward.

**Ceiling:** Height of the lower level of a bank of clouds above the ground.

*Absolute ceiling:* The maximum height above sea level at which a given airplane would be able to maintain horizontal flight under standard air conditions.

*Service ceiling:* The height above sea level, under standard air conditions, at which a given airplane is unable to climb faster than a small specified rate (100 ft per min in the United States and England). This specified rate may differ in different countries.

**Center of pressure of an airfoil:** The point in the chord of an airfoil, prolonged if necessary, which is at the intersection of the chord and the line of action of the resultant air force.

**Center-of-pressure coefficient:** The ratio of the distance of the center of pressure from the leading edge to the chord length.

**Chord:** An arbitrary datum line from which the ordinates and angles of an airfoil are measured. It is usually the straight line tangent to the lower surface at two points, the straight line joining the ends of the mean line, or the straight line between the leading and trailing edges.

**Chord, mean aerodynamic:** The chord of an imaginary airfoil which would have force vectors throughout the flight range identical with those of the actual wing or wings.

**Chord, mean, of a wing:** The quotient obtained by dividing the wing area by the span.

**Cockpit:** An open space in an airplane for the accommodation of pilots or passengers. When completely enclosed, such a space is usually called a cabin.

**Compass:**

*Card (or card magnetic) compass:* A magnetic compass in which the magnets are attached to a pivoted card on which directions are marked.

*Earth-inductor (or induction) compass:* A compass the indications of which depend on the current generated in a coil revolving in the earth's magnetic field.

**Controls:** A general term applied to the means provided to enable the pilot to control the speed, direction of flight, attitude, power, etc., of an aircraft.

**Control stick:** The vertical lever by means of which the longitudinal and lateral control surfaces of an airplane are operated. The elevator is operated by a fore-and-aft movement of the stick; the ailerons, by a side-to-side movement.

**Control surface:** A movable airfoil designed to be rotated or otherwise moved by the pilot in order to change the attitude of the aircraft.

**Cowling:** A removable covering.

**Decalage:** The difference between the angular settings of the wings of a biplane or multiplane. The decalage is measured by the acute angle between the chords in a plane parallel to the plane of symmetry. The decalage is considered positive if the upper wing is set at the larger angle.

**Directional gyro:** A gyroscopic instrument for indicating direction, containing a free gyroscope which holds its position in azimuth and thus indicates angular deviation from the course.

**Dive:** A steep descent, with or without power, in which the air speed is greater than the maximum speed in horizontal flight.

**Downwash:** The air deflected perpendicular to the direction of motion of an airfoil.

**Downwash angle:** *See* **angle, downwash.**

**Drag:** The component of the total air force on a body parallel to the relative wind.

　*Induced drag:* That part of the drag induced by the lift.

　*Parasite drag:* That portion of the drag of an aircraft exclusive of the induced drag of the wings.

　*Profile drag:* The difference between the total wing drag and the induced drag.

　*Profile drag, effective:* The difference between the total wing drag and the induced drag of a wing with the same geometric aspect ratio but elliptically loaded.

**Dynamic lift:** The component of the total aerodynamic force on a body perpendicular to the relative wind.

**Dynamic Pressure:** The product $\frac{1}{2}\rho V^2$, where $\rho$ is the density of the air and $V$ is the relative speed of the air.

**Elevator:** A movable auxiliary airfoil, the function of which is to impress a pitching moment on the aircraft. It is usually hinged to the stabilizer.

**Equivalent monoplane:** A monoplane wing equivalent as to its lift and drag properties to any combination of two or more wings.

**Factor of safety** (stress analysis): The ratio of the ultimate load to any applied load. This term usually refers to the probable minimum factor of safety, which is the ratio of the ultimate load to the probable maximum applied load.

**Fairing:** An auxiliary member or structure whose primary function is to reduce the drag of the part to which it is fitted.

**Feather:** In rotary wing systems, periodically to increase and decrease the incidence of a blade or wing by oscillating the blade or wing about its span axis.

**Fin:** A fixed or adjustable airfoil, attached to an aircraft approximately parallel to the plane of symmetry, to afford directional stability; for example, tail fin, skidfin, etc.

**Fineness ratio:** The ratio of the length of the maximum diameter of a streamline body, as an airship hull.

**Flap:** A hinged or pivoted airfoil forming the rear portion of an airfoil, used to vary the effective camber.

**Flow:**

　*Laminar:* A particular type of streamline flow. The term is usually applied to the flow of a viscous liquid near solid boundaries, when the flow is not turbulent.

*Streamline:* A fluid flow in which the streamlines, except those very near a body and in a narrow wake, do not change with time.

*Turbulent:* Any part of a fluid flow in which the velocity at a given point varies more or less rapidly in magnitude and direction with time.

**Flutter:** An oscillation of definite period but unstable character set up in any part of an aircraft by a momentary disturbance, and maintained by a combination of the aerodynamic, inertial, and elastic characteristics of the member itself (cf. buffeting).

**Fuselage:** The body, of approximately streamline form, to which the wings and tail unit of an airplane are attached.

**Gap:** The distance separating two adjacent wings of a multiplane.

**Glide:** To descend at a normal angle of attack with little or no thrust.

**Glider:** An aircraft heavier than air, similar to an airplane but without a power plant.

**Gyro-horizon:** A gyroscopic instrument that indicates the lateral and longitudinal attitude of the airplane by simulating the natural horizon.

**Gyroplane:** A type of rotor plane whose support in the air is chiefly derived forces, and in which the lift on opposite sides of the plane of symmetry is equalized by rotation of the blades about the blades' axes.

**Helicopter:** A type of rotor plane whose support in the air is normally derived from airfoils mechanically rotated about an approximately vertical axis.

**Horsepower of an engine, rated:** The average horsepower developed by a given type of engine at the rated speed when operating at full throttle, or at a specified altitude or manifold pressure.

**Impact pressure:** The pressure acting at the forward stagnation point of a body such as a pitot tube, placed in an air current. Impact pressure may be measured from an arbitrary datum pressure.

**Instrument flying:** The art of controlling an aircraft solely by the use of instruments; sometimes called "blind flying."

**Interference:** The aerodynamic influence of two or more bodies on one another.

**Landing:** The act of terminating flight in which the aircraft is made to descend, lose flying speed, establish contact with the ground, and finally come to rest.

**Landing gear:** The understructure which supports the weight of an aircraft when in contact with the land or water and which usually contains a mechanism for reducing the shock of landing. Also called "undercarriage."

**Leading edge:** The foremost edge of an airfoil or propeller blade.

**Level off:** To make the flight path of an airplane horizontal after a climb, glide, or dive.

**Lift/drag ratio:** The ratio of the lift to the drag of any body.

**Loading:**

*Power loading:* The gross weight of an airplane divided by the rated horsepower of the engine computed for air of standard density, unless otherwise stated.

*Wing loading:* The gross weight of an airplane divided by the wing area.

**Loop:** A maneuver executed in such a manner that the airplane follows a closed curve approximately in a vertical plane.

**Maneuver:** (a) To operate an aircraft in a skillful manner, so as to cause it to perform evolution out of the ordinary. (b) To perform tactical or acrobatic evolutions with aircraft.

**Maneuverability:** That quality in an aircraft which determines the rate at which its attitude and direction of flight can be changed.

**Margin of safety** (stress analysis): The difference between the ultimate load and any applied load.

**Mean line** (of an airfoil profile): An intermediate line between the upper and lower contours of the profile.

**Monoplane:** An airplane with but one main supporting surface, sometimes divided into two parts by the fuselage.

*High-wing:* A monoplane in which the wing is located at, or near, the top of the fuselage.

*Low-wing:* A monoplane in which the wing is located at, or near, the bottom of the fuselage.

*Midwing:* A monoplane in which the wing is located approximately midway between the top and bottom of the fuselage.

*Parasol:* A monoplane in which the wing is above the fuselage.

**Multiplane:** An airplane with two or more main supporting surfaces placed one above another.

**Nacelle:** An enclosed shelter for personnel or for a power plant. A nacelle is usually shorter than a fuselage, and does not carry the tail unit.

**Nose-down:** To depress the nose of an airplane in flight.

**Noseheavy:** The condition of an airplane in which the nose tends to sink when the longitudinal control is released in any given attitude of normal flight (cf. tailheavy).

**Oscillation:**

*Stable:* An oscillation whose amplitude does not increase.

*Unstable:* An oscillation whose amplitude increases continuously until an attitude is reached from which there is no tendency to return toward the original attitude, the motion becoming a steady divergence.

**Over-all length:** The distance from the extreme front to the extreme rear of an aircraft, including the propeller and the tail unit.

**Pitch:** An angular displacement about an axis parallel to the lateral axis of an aircraft.

**Pitch, angle of:** *See* **angle of pitch.**

**Pitching:** Angular motion about the lateral axis.

**Pitch (or pitching) indicator:** An instrument for indicating the existence and approximate magnitude of the angular velocity about the lateral axis of an aircraft.

**Pitot-static tube:** A parallel or coaxial combination of a pitot and a static tube. The difference between the impact pressure and the static pressure is a function of the velocity of flow past the tube.

**Pitot-tube:** A cylindrical tube with an open end pointed upstream, used in measuring impact pressure.

**Planform, projected:** The contour as viewed from above.

**Profile thickness:** The maximum distance between the upper and lower contours of an airfoil, measured perpendicularly to the mean line of the profile.

**Propeller:** Any device for propelling a craft through a fluid, such as water or air; especially a device having blades which, when mounted on a power-driven shaft, produce a thrust by their action on the fluid.

*Adjustable:* A propeller whose blades are so attached to a mechanism that automatically sets them at their optimum pitch for various flight conditions.

*Automatic:* A propeller whose blades are attached to a mechanism that automatically sets them at their optimum pitch for various flight conditions.

*Controllable:* A propeller whose blades are so mounted that the pitch may be changed while the propeller is rotating.

**Propeller efficiency:** The ratio of the thrust power to the input power of a propeller.

**Propeller rake:** The mean angle which the line joining the centroids of the sections of a propeller blade makes with a plane perpendicular to the axis.

**Propeller root:** That part of the propeller near the hub.

**Propeller thrust:** The component of the total air force on the propeller which is parallel to the direction of advance.

**Propeller thrust, effective:** The net driving force developed by a propeller when mounted on an aircraft, *i.e.*, the actual thrust exerted by the propeller, as mounted on an airplane, minus any increase in the resistance of the airplane due to the action of the propeller.

**Pull-out:** The maneuver of transition from a dive to horizontal flight.

**Range, maximum:** The maximum distance a given aircraft can cover under given conditions, by flying at the economical speed and altitude at all stages of the flight.

**Range at maximum speed:** The maximum distance a given aircraft can fly at full speed at the altitude for maximum speed under given conditions.

**Rate-of-climb indicator:** An instrument that indicates the rate of ascent or descent of an aircraft.

**Reynolds Number:** A non-dimensional coefficient used as a measure of the dynamic scale of a flow.

**Roll:**  An angular displacement about an axis parallel to the longitudinal axis of an aircraft.

**Rolling:**  Angular motion about the longitudinal axis.

**Rotor Plane:**  A form of aircraft whose support in the air is chiefly derived from the vertical component of the force produced by rotating airfoils.

**Rudder:**  A hinged or movable auxiliary airfoil on an aircraft, the function of which is to impress a yawing moment on the aircraft.

**Runway:**  An artificial landing strip permitting the landing and take-off of airplanes under all weather conditions.

**Separation:**  The phenomenon in which the flow past a body placed in a moving stream of fluid separates from the surface of the body.

**Separation point:**  The point at which the separation of the boundary layer begins.

**Sideslipping:**  Motion of an aircraft relative to the air, in which the lateral axis is inclined and the airplane has a velocity component along the lateral axis.  When it occurs in connection with a turn, it is the opposite of skidding.

**Skidding:**  Sliding sidewise away from the center of curvature when turning. It is caused by banking insufficiently, and is the opposite of sideslipping.

**Skin friction:**  The tangential component of the fluid force at a point on a surface.

**Slipstream:**  The current of air driven astern by a propeller.

**Slot:**  The nozzle-shaped passage through a wing whose primary object is to improve the flow conditions at high angles of attack.   It is usually near the leading edge and formed by a main and an auxiliary airfoil, or slat.

**Soar:**  To fly without engine power and without loss of altitude, as does a glider in ascending air currents.

**Span:**  The maximum distance, measured parallel to the lateral axis, from tip to tip of an airfoil, of an airplane wing inclusive of ailerons, or of a stabilizer inclusive of elevator.

**Spin:**  A maneuver in which an airplane descends along a helical path of large pitch and small radius while flying at a mean angle of attach greater than the angle of attack at maximum lift (cf. spiral).

**Spiral:**  A maneuver in which an airplane descends in a helix of small pitch and large radius, the angle of attack being within the normal range of flight angles (cf. spin).

**Stability:**  That property of a body which causes it, when its equilibrium is disturbed, to develop forces or moments tending to restore the original condition.

   *Directional:*  Stability with reference to disturbances about the normal axis of an aircraft, *i.e.*, disturbances which tend to cause yawing.

   *Dynamic:*  That property of an aircraft which causes it, when its state of steady flight is disturbed, to damp the oscillation set up by the restoring forces and moments and gradually return to its original state.

*Lateral:* Stability with reference to disturbances about the longitudinal axis, *i.e.*, disturbances involving rolling or sideslipping. The term "lateral stability" is sometimes used to include both directional and lateral stability, since these cannot be entirely separated.

*Longitudinal:* Stability with reference to disturbances in the plane of symmetry, *i.e.*, disturbances involving pitching and variation of the longitudinal and normal velocities.

*Static:* That property of an aircraft which causes it, when its state of steady flight is disturbed, to develop forces and moments tending to restore its original condition.

**Stabilizer** (airplane): Any airfoil whose primary function is to increase the stability of an aircraft. It usually refers to the fixed horizontal tail surface of an airplane, as distinguished from the fixed vertical surface.

**Stagger:** A term referring to the longitudinal position of the axes of two wings of an airplane. Stagger of any section is measured by the acute angle between a line joining the wing axes and a line perpendicular to the upper wing chord, both lines lying in a plane parallel to the plane of symmetry. The stagger is positive when the upper wing is in advance of the lower.

**Stall:** The condition of an airfoil or airplane in which it is operating at an angle of attack greater than the angle of attack of maximum lift.

**Static pressure:** The force per unit area exerted by a fluid on a surface at rest relative to the fluid.

**Streamline:** The path of a particle of a fluid, supposedly continuous, commonly taken relative to a solid body past which the fluid is moving; generally used only of such flows as are not eddying.

**Supercharger:** A pump for supplying the engine with a greater weight of air of mixture than would normally be inducted at the prevailing atmospheric pressure.

**Sweepback:** The acute angle between a line perpendicular to the plane of symmetry and the plan projection of a reference line in the wing.

**Tail** (airplane): The rear part of an airplane, usually consisting of a group of stabilizing planes, or fins, to which are attached certain controlling surfaces such as elevators and rudders; also called "empennage."

**Tail drag:** A movable or variable weight suspended from the after part of an airship moored to a mast, to aid in restraining the vertical and lateral motions of the stern of the airship.

**Tail surface:** A stabilizing or control surface in the tail of an aircraft.

**Thickness ratio:** The ratio of the maximum thickness of an airfoil section to its chord.

**Trailing edge:** The rearmost edge of an airfoil or of a propeller blade.

**Turn-and-bank indicator:** An instrument combining in one case a turn indicator and a lateral inclinometer.

**Turn indicator:** An instrument for indicating the existence and approximate magnitude of angular velocity about the normal axis of an aircraft.

**Wind, relative:** The velocity of the air with reference to a body in it. It is usually determined from measurements made at such a distance from the body that the disturbing effect of the body upon the air is negligible.

**Wind-tunnel:** An apparatus producing an artificial wind or airstream, in which objects are placed for investigating the air flow about them and the aerodynamic forces exerted on them.

**Wing:** A general term applied to the airfoil, or one of the airfoils, designed to develop a major part of the lift of a heavier-than-air craft.

**Wing profile:** The outline of a wing section.

**Wing section:** A cross-section of a wing parallel to the plane of symmetry or to a specified reference plane.

**Wing tip:** The outer end of an airplane wing.

**Wing-tip rake:** A term referring to the shape of the tip of the wing when the tip edge is sensibly straight in plan but is not parallel to the plane of symmetry. The amount of rake is measured by the acute angle between the straight portion of the wing tip and the plane of symmetry. The rake is positive when the trailing edge is longer than the leading edge.

**Yaw:** An angular displacement about an axis parallel to the normal axis of an aircraft.

**Yawing:** Angular motion about the normal axis.

# Aerodynamic Formula

Aspect Ratio: $b/c = b^2/S$

Bernoulli's Law: $\frac{1}{2}\rho v^2 + p =$ constant along streamline

Stagnation Point: $\frac{1}{2}\rho v^2 = p - p_0$

Density of air at sea level: $\rho_0 = 0.002378$ slug/ft$^3$

Pressure at sea level: $p_0 = 14.7$ lbs/inch$^2 = 2117$ lbs/ft$^2$

Kinematic viscosity at sea level: $\nu = 0.000158$

Reynolds Number: $R = lV/\nu = \rho lV/\mu$

Resistance of flat plate: $D = 1.28 \cdot \frac{1}{2}\rho V^2 S$

Resistance of Wing: $D = C_D \frac{1}{2}\rho V^2 S$

Lift of Wing: $L = C_L \frac{1}{2}\rho V^2 S$

Coefficients $C_D$ and $C_L$ depend on profile, A.R., $\alpha$, and $R$.

Characteristic Curves for A.R. $= 6$.  Correction factors for other A.R.'s

Speed: $V = \sqrt{W/\frac{1}{2}\rho S C_L}$

H.P. $= \bar{D}V = \bar{C}_D \frac{1}{2}\rho V^3 S/550 = (C_D/C_L^{3/2}) \cdot (W^3/\frac{1}{2}\rho S)^{1/2}/550$ where $\bar{D}$ and $\bar{C}_D$ refer to total drag

Gliding Angle: $\tan \gamma = D/L$

Circulation value = vorticity: $\Gamma = \int v_l \cdot dl$

Kutta-Joukowsky's Law: $L = \rho V \Gamma b$

Downwash at wing: $w_0 = (2/\pi b) \cdot \Gamma_{average} = 2L/\rho V b^2 \pi$

Downwash angle: $\tan \varphi_0 = w_0/V = D_i/L$

Lift: $L = w_0 \frac{1}{2}\rho V b^2 \pi = \left(\frac{w_0}{V}\pi \frac{b^2}{S}\right) \cdot \frac{1}{2}\rho V^2 S$

Induced Drag: $D_i = (2/\pi \rho V^2) \cdot (L^2/b^2) = C_L L S/b^2 \pi$

Induced Drag Coefficient: $C_{D_i} = C_L^2 \cdot S/b^2 \pi$

Effective angle of attack: $\alpha_0 = \alpha - C_L S/b^2 \pi$ radians

Biplane Drag: $D_i = (2/\pi \rho V^2) [L_1^2/b_1^2 + L_2^2/b_2^2 + 2\sigma L_1 L_2/b_1 b_2]$

Dynamic Load: $L' = L \cdot V_1^2/V_2^2$

Centrifugal Force: $F = (WV^2/r)$ pdls $= (WV^2/r\ 32.2)$ lbs

# Table of Notations

$a$ = gap

$\alpha$ = angle of attack (alpha)

A.R. = aspect ratio = $b/c = b^2/S$

$b$ = span

$c$ = chord

c.p. = center of pressure

c.g. = center of gravity

$C_L$ = lift coefficient

$C_D$ = drag coefficient

$D$ = drag of wing

$\overline{D}$ = drag of airplane

$D_i$ = induced drag

$\delta$ = thickness of boundary layer (delta)

$F$ = force

$\phi$ = banking angle (phi)

$\varphi$ = downwash angle (phi)

$g$ = 32.2 ft/sec$^2$

$\gamma$ = gliding angle (gamma)

$\Gamma$ = circulation value (capital gamma)

hp = 550 ft lbs/sec

$L$ = lift

$L'$ = dynamic load

$M$ = moment of force or torque

$\mu$ = coefficient of viscosity (mu)

$\nu = \mu/\rho$ = kinematic viscosity (nu)

$n$ = number of revolutions

$p$ = pressure

$\psi$ = angle of yaw (psi)

$R$ = Reynolds number

$\rho$ = density (rho)

$S$ = area

$\sigma$ = coefficient of mutal induction (sigma)

$T$ = thrust

$t$ = time

$\theta$ = angle of pitch (theta)

$V$ = speed, relative wind

$V_0$ = mean wind

$v$ = velocity

$w_0$ = downwash at wing

$w_\infty$ = downwash at infinity

# Index